Worzel Gummic

A Musical

Book and Lyrics by
Keith Waterhouse
and Willis Hall

Music by Denis King

Based upon characters created by
Barbara Euphan Todd

Samuel French - London
New York - Toronto - Hollywood

WORZEL GUMMIDGE

First presented at the Birmingham Repertory Theatre, Birmingham, on 12th December 1980, with the following cast of characters:

Old Farmer	Denis Holmes
The Crowman	Geoffrey Bayldon
Worzel Gummidge	Jon Pertwee
Mr Braithwaite	Lloyd McGuire
Mrs Braithwaite	Mary Griffiths
Sue Peters	Lucy Baker/Cathy Murphy
John Peters	Jonathan Byatt/
	Courtney Roper Knight
Mr Peters	Graham Padden
PC Parsons	Norman Mitchell
Mr Shepherd	Michael Ripper
Aunt Sally	Una Stubbs
Mrs Bloomsbury-Barton	Jane Freeman
Vicar	Jon Cartwright
Miss Lewisham	Susan Jane Tanner
Sergeant Beetroot	Denis Holmes
Soggy Boggart	Jonathan Stephens
Scabby Tater Blight	Mark Finesilver
Saggy Tatersack	Jon Cartwright
Scarecrows,	Denise Baxter,
Morris Dancers,	Jon Cartwright,
Farmhands	Julie Edmett, Paul Edward,

Lynn Emeny, Lilian Evans,
Chris Eymard, Mike Finesilver,
Marcus MacKenzie, Christopher Robinson,
Emma Rogers, Howard Samuels,
Jonathan Stephens, Susan Jane Tanner,
Kay Townsend

Directed by Clive Perry
Settings by Geoffrey Scott
Musical direction by Ray Bishop

The version on which this Acting Edition is based, was presented by Duncan C. Weldon, for Triumph Productions Ltd, by arrangement with Louis I. Michaels Ltd and in association with Paul Gregg and Lionel Becker, at the Cambridge Theatre, London, on 22nd December 1981, with the following cast of characters:

Crowman	Geoffrey Bayldon
Mr Braithwaite	Jon Cartwright
Mrs Braithwaite	Mary Griffiths
Sue	Lucy Baker/
	Lucinda Cahn
John	Jonathan Byatt/
	Steven Gallagher
Mr Peters	Graham Padden
Worzel Gummidge	Jon Pertwee
PC Parsons	Norman Mitchell
Mr Shepherd	Frank Marlborough
Aunt Sally	Una Stubbs
Mrs Bloomsbury-Barton	Jo Kendall
Vicar	Jonathan Stephens
Miss Lewisham	Lynne Hockney
Sergeant Beetroot	Bill Pertwee
Soggy Boggart	Jonathan Stephens
Scabby Taterblight	Mark Finesilver
Hessian Tatersack	Jon Cartwright
Scarecrows, Villagers	Denny Baxter,
	Sally Carpenter,

Lynn Emeny, Marcus Mackenzie, Christopher Robinson, Howard Samuels, Kay Townsend

Directed by Clive Perry
Settings by Geoffrey Scott
Musical directions by Ian Macpherson

The action takes place on Scatterbrook Farm and the surrounding countryside

MUSICAL NUMBERS
ACT I

1	**Overture**	Orchestra
2	**Scarecrow's Hymn (Version I)**	Crowman, Scarecrow
3	**In The Country**	Villagers
3A	**Music Link**	Orchestra
3B	**Music Link**	Orchestra
4	**One 'Ead An' An 'Ead**	Worzel, John, Sue
4A	**Music Link—One 'Ead An' An 'Ead**	Orchestra
5	**Aunt Sally's Song**	Aunt Sally
5A	**Morris Dance I**	Orchestra
5B	**Morris Dance II**	Orchestra
5C	**Hurry Music**	Orchestra
6	**Why Should She Choose A Scarecrow?**	Worzel
6A	**Morris Dance III**	Orchestra
7	**Chase Him (Version I)**	Villagers, Mr Braithwaite, Vicar, Mr Peters, Mrs Bloomsbury-Barton
8	**Slice Of Cake**	Worzel, Aunt Sally, John, Sue
9	**Aunt Sally's Dance**	Orchestra
9A	**Music Link**	Orchestra
9B	**Music Link**	Orchestra
9C	**Chase Him (Instrumental Reprise)**	Orchestra
10	**Chase Him (Version II)**	Villagers, Mrs Bloomsbury-Barton, Mr Peters
10A	**Music Link**	Orchestra
11	**It'll Suit Us**	Worzel, Aunt Sally
11A	**Music Link—Sting**	Orchestra
12	**Why Should She Choose A Scarecrow? (Reprise)**	Worzel

ACT II

13	**Opening Act II**	Orchestra
14	**Scarecrow Day**	Scarecrows, John, Sue
14A	**Spooky Music Link**	Orchestra
15	**Make Yourself A Friend**	Crowman
16	**We'll Be There**	Sergeant Beetroot, Scabby, Soggy
16A	**Scarecrow's March**	Worzel
17	**Aunt Sally's Song (Reprise)**	Aunt Sally
17A	**Rescue Music**	Orchestra
17B	**Rookroster Day (Instrumental)**	Orchestra
18	**Scarecrow's Hymn (Version II)**	Crowman, Scarecrows
18A	**Music**	Orchestra
18B	**Eerie Music**	Orchestra

PRODUCTION NOTE

This Acting Edition is based on the production as performed at the Cambridge Theatre where elaborate staging facilities were available, enabling scenery to be flown. However, this is not essential and the staging is left to the imagination of the individual director and the resources available. Whether the staging is simple or elaborate it is important that the scene changes are quick and fluent to ensure continuity.

The detailed routine of "The Rescue of Aunt Sally from Mr Shepherd's Cottage", as performed in the London production, is included on pages 49 and 50 as no more than a guide-line.

ACT I
Scene 1

Ten Acre Field. Just before dawn

No. 1. Overture

A newly-made Scarecrow, still minus its head, stands on a scarecrow pole with a commanding view of Ten Acre Field

Out of the early mist emerges the Crowman pedalling his tricycle. He dismounts, takes a scarecrow head out of his basket, and holds it up against the headless figure

Crowman I wonder ... Out of all the hundreds of scarecrows I've made, something tells me that this one's going to be trouble ... Maybe I should pull it to pieces and start again. But what a waste of a good mangel worzel ... No: we'll go on with the ceremony.

The Crowman makes a couple of mystical gesticulations. We see a flash of lightning and hear the rumble of thunder

A number of grotesque Scarecrows appear from out of the mist in ungainly fashion, hugging the shadows—they are hardly more than silhouettes

When they have settled themselves into a wide, rigid, silent circle, the Crowman nods

Well met, my children. (*He holds the scarecrow head up ritualistically as he sings*)

No. 2. Scarecrow's Hymn (Version I)

Apples for health,
Corn for plenty,
Sunshine and snow,
Ten years or twenty,
Berries for happiness,
Hazelnuts for thrifty,
Seasons come and go,
Thirty then fifty.

Scarecrows

Holly for everlasting,
Mistletoe for mystery;
Only the scarecrows know
That the future is history.

The Crowman fixes the head on the scarecrow's shoulders. He takes a twig from his pocket and breaks it over the Scarecrow's head as:

Crowman (*speaking*) Apples for health,
                        Corn for plenty,
                        Berries for happiness,
                        By the wind and the rain and all the seasons . . .
                        I name this scarecrow Worzel Hedgerow Gummidge.

A tremendous cawing from the rooks overhead. A murmur of approval from the Scarecrows. The Crowman removes his hat and becomes even more solemn

Worzel Gummidge, I am the Crowman. As rain is to the crops, and wind to the seeds, as the sun is to the berries, so is the Crowman to all things of twigs and straw. And I give thee life . . .

Another crack of thunder. The Scarecrow lurches forward on its post. Thunder and lightning, and the sky darkens into blackness

The Scarecrows melt away

Worzel Gummidge comes to life

Worzel—face me. Arms down. Follow me. Now walk.

Worzel totters dangerously close to the edge of the stage

Worzel! Worzel! Now over the stile—I think you know where to go.

Worzel moves off to take up his appointed place in Ten Acre Field

SCENE 2

Scatterbrook Farm. A summer's day

The farmyard has a farmhouse with some washing hanging outside, a gypsy caravan, and a stile overlooking Ten Acre Field

Farm labourers and young folk from the village enter from all directions and cross on their way to or from the fields, singing

No. 3. In the Country

All   Busy bees are in a tizzy
         Gath'rin' honey, ain't it funny
         In the country.
         Every swallow takes a swallow-dive
         And soars across a field of waving corn,
         Every daisy
         Feels a little crazy,
         Every buttercup blesses the day that it was ever born.

Every season there's a reason
Why we're glad not sad we're livin'
In the country.
Every day we say we wouldn't choose
To lose this way of life we live at all.
Every dawning, every bright new morning,
Oh say isn't it great to state the country life's a ball.

Boys Country's living's
A way of giving
Everyone a smile,
Every country mile.

Girls Country dwellin's
A way of sellin'

All That old life-style,
It gets you in a while.

Boys Every day in every way
We're proud to shout hooray, we're livin'
In the country.
There's no reason why as time goes by
We'll ever change the way we live at all.
Girls Every morning,
Each and every dawning,
We will shout it about that livin' the country life's a ball.

All Every morning,
Each and every dawning,
We will shout it about that livin' the country life's a ball,
We will shout it about that livin' the country life's a ball.

As the song ends, Mr Peters enters carrying a couple of bulging suitcases. He is followed by his two children, John and Sue both carrying their personal possessions and looking over their shoulders towards Ten Acre Field and the Scarecrow

John It *did* wave, I tell you—I saw it!
Sue You can't have done, 'cos it didn't.
John Yes it did!
Sue No, it didn't!
Mr Peters Will you pair give it a rest? Mrs Braithwaite'll think I've brought a pair of Kilkenny cats down to live in her caravan! Well, what do you think of your new home?

During the following Mrs Braithwaite comes out of the farmhouse

John Fantastic! Bags I the top bunk.
Sue That's not fair. I've bagged the top bunk.
John No you haven't, because I bagged it first.
Sue No you didn't, because I bagged it before you even saw it.

John *I* bagged it before we even left London!

Mrs Braithwaite Are they always argufying like this, Mr Peters?

Mr Peters Never stop from morning till night. Do you know what they were on about a minute ago? Whether that blooming scarecrow waved to them or not!

Mrs Braithwaite You may laugh, Mr Peters, but I'll swear there've been moonlight nights when I've looked out of that bedroom window and *I've* seen it waving.

Fascinated reaction from the children. Mr Peters, jerking his head in their direction, coughs discreetly

Mrs Braithwaite Oh dear me—I forgot there were young ears flapping. Do they suffer from nightmares?

Sue ⎫ *(together)* ⎰ John does—I don't.
John ⎰   ⎱ Sue does—I don't.

Mrs Braithwaite It's just the breeze, children, that's all it is. And if you hear any village gossip about Rookroster Day, take no notice. Because if you listen to what some daft folk round here have to say, they'd have you believe they've seen that scarecrow walking about on Rookroster Day.

Mr Peters (*to the children, hastily changing the subject*) Why don't you two make yourselves useful and get all this stuff into the caravan?

Mrs Braithwaite Then you can have a look round Scatterbrook while I make you a nice farmhouse tea. Do they eat scones with strawberry jam and cream, Mr Peters?

Mr Peters They eat anything that's put in front of them, Mrs B.

The children begin to load the suitcases into the caravan

Mr Braithwaite appears. He is about to cross the farmyard when Mrs Braithwaite calls him over

Mrs Braithwaite Jack! Don't go sidling off like that—come and meet our visitors.

Mr Peters How de do.

Mr Braithwaite Pleased to meet you. Hope the caravan suits.

Sue It's smashing. Can I have the top bunk?

Mr Peters Please.

Sue Please.

Mr Peters Yes, if you like.

Behind his back Sue pulls her tongue out at John

John That's not fair, *I* bagged it.

Mr Peters You can toss up for it.

John pulls a triumphant face at Sue. Over the following they toss a coin. Sue wins, grimaces her satisfaction, and they go into the caravan

Mr Braithwaite It's not Buckingham Palace but it should be comfortable enough.

Mr Peters It'll do very well till we've had a look round.

Mr Braithwaite (*about to move off*) Well, I've got my work to do.

Mrs Braithwaite If you're going across Ten Acre, Jack, will you do something? Will you prove to John and Sue that our old scarecrow's just made of rags and straw? Because they suffer from nightmares, apparently.

Mr Peters No more than most kids, Mrs B!

Mrs Braithwaite Just show them that it can't walk about on moonlight nights.

Mr Braithwaite I wish it would—and keep on walking till it's out of sight. Then I could get me a proper electric rook-scarer.

Mr Peters You don't see many scarecrows these days, Mrs B.

Mrs Braithwaite Oh, there's quite a few around these parts, Mr Peters. There's a funny old man makes them and looks after them. The Crowman, he's known as. You'll meet some strange folk in the countryside—it'll make a change from London.

During the following, Mr Braithwaite follows the track across Ten Acre and then stands by the Scarecrow

A Labourer enters at the same time and joins Mr Braithwaite

Mr Peters I hope so. That's what I'm looking for, now they don't have their mother. Too many busybodies up there, interfering. Think a father can't bring up his own children. (*Peering into the caravan*) No eating sweets before tea! (*Firmly*) Well—just five each and no more. (*Triumphantly to Mrs Braithwaite*) You have to be cruel to be kind, sometimes.

Mr Braithwaite (*calling down*) Hoy!

Mrs Braithwaite Just come out here a minute, children.

Mr Peters Come on!

They come out of the caravan

Mrs Braithwaite Now then. Do you still think that scarecrow waved to you?

Sue } (*together*) { No!
John } { Yes!

Mr Peters Just watch Mr Braithwaite.

Mrs Braithwaite waves a handkerchief. To a roll of drums, Mr Braithwaite pulls off the head of the Scarecrow and holds it aloft

Mrs Braithwaite There you see! It's nothing but a mangel-worzel with a hat on.

Mr Braithwaite puts the head down on the ground by the side of the Scarecrow, and moves off, followed by the Labourer

Mr Peters (*looking at his watch*) My goodness, it's nearly opening time—I mean it's nearly tea-time.

Mrs Braithwaite Of course.

Mr Peters I'd better go and shift that car of mine, Mrs B. Then I think I'll just drive down to the village and see if I can find—er—a petrol station.

Mrs Braithwaite On the right—next to the *George and Dragon*.

Mr Peters Very convenient.

Sue Can we come, Dad?

Mrs Braithwaite I'm sure your father doesn't want you hanging about outside the—petrol station. Off you go and look round the farm while I put an apple pie in the oven.

Mr Peters (*pointing off*) And don't walk on any of those crops.

Mrs Braithwaite That's grass, Mr Peters.

Mr Peters Yes. Well . . . Don't walk on any grass.

Mrs Braithwaite goes into the farmhouse

Mr Peters moves off towards the stile

John (*calling after him*) Dad? Will you bring us back some crisps and lemonade—from the petrol station?

Mr Peters We'll see.

Sue Come on—let's see if there's any horses to ride.

No. 3A. Music Link

John and Sue run off in the opposite direction from Mr Peters

Mr Peters crosses Ten Acre. He stops by the Scarecrow, picks up its head and replaces it—but the wrong way round. After trying for a moment to get it in the right position he gives up and moves off

Mrs Braithwaite, stirring pastry mixture in a bowl, comes out of the farmhouse and looks up at the sky. Feeling drops of rain she takes her washing into the farmhouse

John and Sue appear over the brow of Ten Acre

Scene 3

Ten Acre Field

John and Sue stop by the Scarecrow. The sky is darkening

John Pooh! I can still pong those pigs!

Sue That's not the pigs' pong. It's those cows in the next field.

John (*counting*) Four . . . eight . . . twelve . . . sixteen cows. That's seventy-five animals we've seen altogether.

Sue Seventy-four.

John Seventy-five.

Sue Only if you count that field-mouse we saw in the barn.

John It wasn't a field-mouse, it was a rat—and I *am* counting it.

Sue It wasn't a rat, it was a field-mouse.

John Anyway, it's still seventy-five.

Sue Seventy-four. Seventy-four boring animals and one boring scarecrow. It's not a very interesting farm, is it?

John What did you expect—elephants and chimpanzees?

Sue Horses. It's not a proper farm without horses. As for that thing—it's not even a proper scarecrow.

John I still say it waved.

Sue It can't have done—it's made of straw. It's the most boring scarecrow I've ever seen. And it's coming on to rain. Come on, let's see if tea's ready.

John In a minute—I want to see if it waves again.

Sue John—it's going to *pour* down in a minute!

John That's all right—we'll borrow the scarecrow's umbrella. Do you suppose it'll mind? (*He takes the umbrella*)

Sue (*sarcastically*) Why don't you ask it?

John Excuse me, mister—can we borrow your umbrella?

No. 3B. Music Link

The Scarecrow abruptly lurches forward, and from within its straw innards croaks a strange, deep, rural voice

Worzel Oo ar!

Momentarily petrified, the children stare at the Scarecrow, then at each other

   John—clutching the umbrella—and Sue run for it

Thunder and lightning

   Farm workers of both sexes, wearing sou' westers and wellington boots, run home through the rain

Black-out

SCENE 4

The Barn and Hayloft

The scarecrow pole in Ten Acre Field is now uninhabited

The Lights come up to give a bright morning effect on John and Sue who are flopped out on bales of hay in the barn, reading comics. The rooks are cawing

Worzel Gummidge, stiffly climbing the stile, crosses the farmyard, screwing his head the right way round, and enters the barn where he sees the children

Worzel Well I'll be bumswizzled! 'Ere, W-wor H-wor E-wor R-wor E-wor S-wor*zel*-M-wor Y-wor —what you lookin' at me like that for? Don't none of you talk Worzelese? Huh, what an iggerant lot of yewmans you is! Well I'll just 'ave to talk in yakkity then, won't I? What I wants to know is, what have you done with my umbrelly? Oy!

The children lower their comics and stare at him, speechless and mesmerized

   Oy! I'm talkin' to 'ee! What have you done with my umbrelly?

John, in trepidation, hands over the umbrella

   (*Grabbing it*) Ar. Hand it over then. Let me have a look. (*He puts it up and examines its tattered frame*) No 'arm done. (*Turning to John he puts on a hideous smile*) Morning, mister.

John Good—good-morning.

Worzel Sir. Good-morning, *sir*, that's what you should call me, me being older nor you, see?

John Sorry, sir. Good-morning, sir.

Worzel Either that, or as it might be, good-morning, Mr Gummidge. Mr Worzel Gummidge. That being my name, see ... (*After an expectant pause*) You lot is too 'igh an' mighty to 'ave names, I expecks?

John This is Sue, sir, and I'm John.

Worzel Ar—John is it? I've known a few Johns hereabouts. Thieves mostly—vagabonds what steals other people's umbrellys.

John We were going to bring it back.

Worzel Sir!

John Sir!

Worzel So you says. Well, don't I get invited for a sit-down then, an' a cup o' tea an' a slice o' cake?

John We haven't got any cake, sir, Worzel, sir.

Sue I could go over to the farmhouse and get some.

Worzel Go on, then. Hop it. A big slice, mind. Plum cake, if there is any, and if there ain't any plum cake I'll 'ave pound cake, seed cake, simnel cake, Christmas cake, weddin' cake, christenin' cake, upside-down cake or right-side-up cake. Well go on then!

Sue exits

(*Turning pointedly to John*) Well? Where's your manners, young feller-me-lad?

John Oh. Sorry, sir. Would you like to sit down for a minute, sir?

Worzel I might sit down for a minute. I might sit down for 'alf an hour. We shall 'ave to see. 'Ow do?

John (*puzzled, politely extending his hand*) How do you do.

Worzel Not 'ow do you do! We've done all that! I said 'ow *do*! 'Ow do you sit down?

John Don't you *know* how to sit down?

Worzel It just so 'appens as it's slipped my mind. 'Cos I ain't got my rememberin' 'ead on, see?

John Your remembering head?

Worzel Ain't you never 'eard of a rememberin' 'ead afore?

John No, sir!

Worzel Oo ar—o' course! You yewmans only 'ave one 'ead apiece, don't you? I was forgettin' that—not 'aving my rememberin' 'ead on, see? Now then, about this 'ere sittin' down ...

John It's easy. You do it like this. (*He sits down on a bale of hay*)

Worzel Easy, is it? Oh I'll have a go at that, then. (*With a great deal of palaver he copies John*) There y'are. Ar. 'Ow's that? Not bad, eh, considerin' us scarecrows ain't supposed to sit down at all?

Sue returns with a hot apple pie which she has just purloined from the farmhouse

Sue Then you really *are* a scarecrow?

Worzel 'Course I's a scarecrow! What's I look like—the King o' Russia? My my my, that smells good, that do!

Sue It's an apple pie but you can't eat it yet because it's just come out of the oven.

Worzel Well blow on it then! (*Slapping his "stumick"*) And you stop your scritchin' an' scratchin'—you'll get your crumbs when ol' Worzel's good an' ready! (*He produces a robin from the depths of his straw, wipes his nose with it, and replaces it*)

John That's a live bird!

Worzel Little Robin Redbreast, that is. I uses 'er as my handychief. She don't mind, long as she gets 'er grub nice and regular. Lives in my stumick, so she does. 'Cept when I walks about, then 'er gets all fidgety-widgety.

Sue Have you always walked about, Mister Gummidge?

Worzel Oo ar! Leastways up, ever since I got born.

John I never knew scarecrows got born before, I thought they were made.

Worzel That's what I'm telling you—the Crowman, he makes us. First we gets made—then we gets born. That way, see, we don't grow out of our clothes—not like you titchy yewmans, what has to have a new pair o' trowsis every year. And after we's been born, that's our birthday, see? Just like it's mine today. (*Pointedly*) My birthday today. Well—what are you waiting for?

Sue Many happy returns.

Worzel Never mind 'appily returns. Where's my prezzie?

John It's rude to ask for presents.

Sue Anyway, we didn't know.

Worzel I'll just have to make do with that there pie, then. Give it 'ere.

Sue It's still too hot. (*To John*) And don't tell Dad who took it off Mrs Braithwaite's window-sill.

Worzel Why's she allus cookin' an' bakin' an' fryin' an' stewin' for that there farmer. Tain't fair. And never a scrap for ol' Worzel, who spends all day scaring her crows away.

Sue She cooks for Mr Braithwaite because she's his wife.

Worzel 'Is wife, is she? I've 'eard tell o' wifes. I shall get me a wife meself one o' these days, then I'll get bacon an' eggs for me breakfast. An' cups o' tea an' slices o' cake for me tea.

John Scarecrows can't *really* get married, can they?

Worzel What's to stop 'em?

Sue Will you marry a lady scarecrow, Mr Gummidge?

Worzel I might do, then again—I might not. I shall have to think about it. (*He moves up a ladder to the hayloft*) In fack I shall think about it this very minute. Juss' as soon as I c'n find my thinking 'ead.

Sue Your *thinking* head?

John *And* he has a remembering head. Haven't you, Worzel? Sir?

Worzel Th'ass right. An' I'd show it to you too—on'y I can't remember where it is. But I got lots an' lots o' 'eads. (*He holds them up one by one*) This one's my Swedish circus 'ead—'cos it's made out of a swede an' not a

mangel-worzel. This one's my turnip magician's head—bet you don't
know whey it's called a turnip 'ead.

Sue Because it's made out of a turnip?

Worzel No—because I never know where it's going to "turnup" next!

The children voice their disapproval at the bad joke

An' this 'ere's my riddle-me-ree 'ead. When is a door not a door? Find out
for yourself, you silly ol' fossil! An' this 'ere's my 'appy 'ead—for when I
get's married. Now what have we got down 'ere?

*During the following, Worzel turns his back and acquires a new "head"—
probably a quick-change device of hat with fixed glasses, whiskers etc.*

Sue I wish I had a happy head for Monday mornings!

John I wish *I* had a magician's head—I'd vanish the school!

Sue Or even a dancing head—and then I could do ballet!

John How about a footballer's head—for heading in goals!

Worzel Ta-raaa! (*He turns back to them and looks totally different*)

John Crikey!

Sue Is that your teaching head?

Worzel Teaching head nothing. It's me learnin' 'ead—for doin' sums an'
knowin' 'ow to count: one an' one is one an' another one is another
one . . .

Sue That's not counting, Worzel.

Worzel Yes it is too.

John I bet you can't count at all.

Worzel 'Oo can't? Pin your lug-'oles back, Mister Clever-clogs—I'll show
you 'ow to count!

*During the following song, Worzel picks up and puts down heads with startling
rapidity as he sings*

No. 4. One 'Ead An' An 'Ead

(*Singing*)	One 'ead an' an 'ead adds up to some 'eads
Kids	Two!
Worzel	An' two 'eads an' an 'ead adds up to more
Kids	Three!
Worzel	An' three 'eads an' an 'ead makes an awful lot of 'eads
Kids	Four!
Worzel	An' four 'eads an' an 'ead so I've often 'eard it said
	Gives you more 'eads than you've ever seen before
Kids	Five!
Worzel	Five 'eads an' an 'ead is more'n plenty
Kids	Six!
Worzel	An' six 'eads an' an 'ead is twenty-three
Kids	Seven!
Worzel	An' if seven 'eads is your pleasure,
	An' you adds one for good measure,
	Now 'ow many 'eads is that, now let me see . . .

Kids   Eight!

Worzel (*speaking*) I wor juss' goin' to say eight if you'd given me 'arf a
chance—you've made me lose count—we shall have to go back to the
beginning now! (*He sings*)

	One 'ead an' an 'ead adds up to some 'eads
Kids	Two!
Worzel	An' two 'eads an' an 'ead adds up to more
Kids	Three!
Worzel	An' three 'eads an' an 'ead makes an awful lot of 'eads
Kids	Four!
Worzel	An' four 'eads an' an 'ead, so I've often 'eard it said,
	Gives you more 'eads that you've ever seen before
Kids	Five!
Kids	Five 'eads an' an 'ead is more'n plenty
Kids	Six!
Worzel	An' six 'eads an' an 'ead is twenty-three
Kids	Seven!
Worzel	An' if seven 'eads is your pleasure,
	An' you adds one for good measure,
	Now 'ow many 'eads is that, now let me see . . .
Kids	Eight!
Worzel	An' this is where we're gettin' to the 'ard part
	'Cos the more you adds it's 'arder, you'll agree?
Kids	Certainlee!
Worzel	In a book somewheres I've read,
	Take eight 'eads an' add an 'ead
	An' you 'as a score or more 'eads
	Easilee.
Kids	Nine!
Worzel	Nine 'eads in-a-line 'eads doin' fine 'eads,
	Add another 'ead to nine 'eads
	Carefulee.
Kids	Ten!
Worzel	Are you really sure it's ten?
Kids	Shall we do it all again?
Worzel	No!
	Dangblast it, you can count as well as me!

At the end of the song, Worzel grabs the apple-pie from Sue

Worzel An' now I'll 'ave that pie!
Sue It's not all for you! Bring it back!

No. 4A. Music Link—One 'Ead An' An 'Ead

Pursued by Sue and John, Worzel runs off with the pie

SCENE 5

Outside Mr Shepherd's Cottage

The cottage features a large attic window with a balcony through which we can see Mr Shepherd, an irascible and money-grubbing village personality, flicking at the Aunt Sally figure with a feather-duster. Mr Shepherd draws the curtains, hiding himself and the Aunt Sally figure from view

Over the above, PC Parsons, the village constable, cycles on with some rolled-up posters and a pot of paste. He begins pasting a poster—which advertises a village fête and includes a prominent picture of the Aunt Sally—on the side of the cottage

Mr Shepherd comes out of his front door and points grumpily to the No bill stickers *sign*

Mr Shepherd Can't you read, Police Constable Parsons?

PC Parsons 'Afternoon, Mr Shepherd.

Mr Shepherd Never mind good-afternoons. You're supposed to uphold the law in these parts—not go round committing a public nuisance.

PC Parsons It's for charity, Mr Shepherd.

Mr Shepherd Charity begins at home, Police Constable Parsons. And who gave you permission to use a likeness of my Aunt Sally on that poster—because I certainly didn't.

PC Parsons steps back and examines the picture on the poster as though looking at it for the first time

PC Parsons Is *that* who it is? Your Auntie Annie?

Mr Shepherd Aunt *Sally*, PC Parsons!

PC Parsons And is she opening the fête then? That'll put Mrs Bloomsbury-Barton's nose out of joint!

Mr Shepherd Course she ain't opening the fête—she's the main attraction! She ain't a real live person—she's a wooden dummy. She's a valuable antique!

The curtained attic window is thrown open to reveal the real Aunt Sally. During the following she primps and preens herself. She is unseen by Mr Shepherd and PC Parsons—nor do they hear her interjections

Aunt Sally Absolutely priceless! A jewel beyond compare!

Mr Shepherd I haven't made my mind up yet about letting her appear at the fête—her's worth too much money to be used as a bloomin' coconut shy!

Aunt Sally The idea's quite ridiculousless!

Mr Shepherd Do you know how long that figure's been in my family?

PC Parsons No—but I don't doubt you'll tell me!

Mr Shepherd I'll tell you—donkey's years! Do you know how we came by it?

Aunt Sally I was left to him in a duke's will.

Mr Shepherd My grandfather got it from a travelling showman who was camping on his land.

Aunt Sally A proper gentleman that showman—we travelled everywhere—
ai've appeared before all the crowned heads of Europe.

Mr Shepherd He got lost coming from Doncaster. Drunk, my grandfather
always reckoned. He took the wooden dummy off him for trespassing.

PC Parsons Have you ever thought of showing it to Miss Lewisham? Her
that keeps the antique shop in Market Steeplebury? She goes in for this
fairground stuff, you know. Sends a lot of it to America.

Aunt Sally Americky? How vulgar. Nasty common town from all I've
heard. Give me Bulgaria any day.

Mr Shepherd Pays well, does she?

PC Parsons I believe so. She's coming over to the village fête on Saturday—
so if she spots your Aunt Mary there she might give you a price for it.

Mr Shepherd Aunt Sally! And I ain't said for definite she'll be there yet!

PC Parsons Think about it, Mr Shepherd.

Mr Shepherd I'll tell you what I'll do, Police Constable Parsons—I'll think
about it.

Mr Shepherd goes back indoors. PC Parsons cycles off

Aunt Sally remains at the window

Aunt Sally Of course, if they'd consulted me in the matter, I could 'ave told
them I haven't the slightest intention of being bought and sold like a
pound of sugar. The whole idea's prepospospos. *Ay* wasn't carved out of
the finest mahogany to be bought and sold—*or* to have wooden balls
chucked at my pretty 'ead, come to that. *Ay* was intended to marry a duke
and live in a grand house with a ha-ha and *pomme frites* for breakfast. It's
just a question of waiting for Mr Right to come along, that's all. (*She
sings*)

No. 5. Aunt Sally's Song

He's as rich as can be
All he needs now is me,
He's dashing, he's brainier
Than the prince of Rumania,
Two oil-wells in Prussia,
A new yacht each week,
A salt-mine in Russia,
Perhaps he's a sheik,
Who vanquishes dragons,
He wears bright shining armour . . .

*Worzel Gummidge enters and, enraptured, removes his hat and stares up at
Aunt Sally*

One thing he doesn't do
Is work for a farmer.

Worzel Oy! How where 'as I seen you afore?

Aunt Sally Nowhere, I shouldn't wonder. Ay'm far too grand to mix with
the likes of you.

Worzel Wait a minute—I knows where I's seen you. 'Avin' wooden balls chucked at your 'ead at the travellin' fair—years an' years ago. You're Aunt Sally.

Aunt Sally One *did* used to do a little charity work with a travelling fair—but I'm quite sure we haven't been introduced.

Worzel Ar. Then I'll interdooce miself. H-wor-O-wor-W-wor-dip, D-wor-O-wor-dip. I'm Worzel Gummidge. W-wor-O-wor-z-wor-e-wor-l-wor-zel, G-wor-u-wor-m-wor-m-wor-i-wor-d-wor-g-wor-e-worzel.

Aunt Sally Ay'm very sorry, but I don't speak scarecrow language. I was brought up too nice.

Worzel What do 'ee speak then?

Aunt Sally Romany, of course. Like what the gypsies talk. The very best gypsies, that is. I also talk la-di-dah fluently.

Worzel Ar. Now *I* talk la-di-dah effluently but I ain't got my la-di-dah 'ead on, see? What else do 'ee speak?

Aunt Sally English, naturally.

Worzel English. Ar, that's one langwidge I doesn't know. Never 'eard o' English.

Aunt Sally It's what we're talking now, stupid.

Worzel Oo ar, is it? I've allus called it yakkity. On account of that's the way they talks it—yakkity yakkity yakkity. 'Ow come you can talk yakkity, when you've got a wooden 'ead?

Aunt Sally Don't be impertinent.

Worzel A very *nice* wooden 'ead, Aunt Sally. In fack—the bestest wooden 'ead I's ever seen . . .

Aunt Sally Flattery from a walking, talking bag of straw! How ridicoulous-lous . . . (*She sings*)

> Is it too much to ask?
> Am I up to the task?
> For my dreams of a fair beau
> Rise higher than a scarecrow,
> This prince that I seek,
> This man amongst men,
> He's brave, he's not weak,
> His strength is as ten,
> He'll sweep me off my feet,
> He can right any wrong
> And he doesn't wear clothes
> That are cast-offs—and pong . . .

Worzel If I got a new suit o' clothes, Aunt Sally, would you marry me?

Aunt Sally *Marry* you?

Worzel Oo ar. An' cook me bacon an' eggs for me breakfast an' cups o' tea an' slices o' cake for me tea.

Aunt Sally Cook you bacon and eggs? I'll have you know that when *I* get married, I'll have footmen and butlers to cook bacon and eggs. And parlourmaids and pantrymaids to attend to the cups of tea and slices o' cake . . . (*She sings*)

> Will I find him at last,
> Is he future or past?
> He's bursting with graces,
> How handsome his face is,
> The hero I'm after,
> My keepsake he'll keep,
> I'll cherish his laughter,
> If he weeps I'll weep.
> Suppose I don't meet him
> Well—that's how life goes . . .

Worzel So is your answer yes or no, then?
Aunt Sally   No!
> For I never could marry
> A thing that scares crows.

She slams the window and draws the curtains

Worzel Aunt Sally, I'll tell'ee what I'll do—No I won't, 'cos she ain't there. (*Trudging desolately away he comes across the poster pasted up by PC Parsons*) My my my! What an 'andsome picture o' Aunt Sally there. I specks she 'ad it specially painted for all 'er visitors to look at when she's away from 'ome, 'aving wooden balls chucked at 'er 'ead . . . (*Trying to read*) "EGALLVI EFTE? Don't make sense . . . I knows what I'll do. I'll take it 'ome and let me reading 'ead 'ave a go at it. (*He starts to peel the poster off the wall*)

PC Parsons enters wheeling his bicycle with the pot of paste on the handlebars

PC Parsons (*coming up behind Worzel*) You can keep on walking till you're out of the village. We don't want your sort round here.
Worzel An' what's wrong with my sort, I should like to know?
PC Parsons Any more lip from you, my lad, and I'll have you in for questioning.
Worzel Yer toffee nosed, puffed up, cross-eyed toad.
PC Parsons What did you say?
Worzel I sez I'll be off to the bus stop across the road.
PC Parsons See that you do—and if they won't let you on the bus try the council dust cart.

Worzel begins to shuffle off

(*Regarding the poster which is half-pulled from the wall*) Blooming vandals!

Putting the pot of paste on the ground he bends to dip the brush in it to repair the damage. The target is irresistible to Worzel. Taking aim, he boots PC Parsons in the rear

Worzel runs off

(*Racing after him; yelling*) Come back here! You just wait till I get my hands on you! You'll get six months for this, that's what you'll get ...!

SCENE 6

Scatterbrook Farm and the edge of the Village Fête

The day of the village fête—as proclaimed by the colourful banners and streamers dropped from the flies

No. 5A. Morris Dance I

A team of morris dancers on their way to the fête dance by, practising as they go with shrill cries from their leader of "Do come along!" etc. As the morris dancers pass, the children, wearing their best clothes, emerge from the caravan

John ⎱
Sue ⎰ (*together*) Come on, Dad, we'll be late!

Mrs Braithwaite comes out of the farmhouse, carrying a basket of cakes for the fête

Mrs Braithwaite You've got oodles of time—they haven't even got all the tents up yet. Now who's going to carry this basket of butterfly buns for the tea-tent?
Sue (*taking the basket*) I will, Mrs Braithwaite.

Mr Peters emerges from the caravan wearing a straw boater and multi-striped blazer. He strikes a pose

Mr Peters Ta-ra! How do I look?

John and Sue exchange glances and suppress giggles

Mrs Braithwaite (*tactfully*) Very dapper, I must say.

Mrs Braithwaite goes back into the farmhouse

Sue (*showing him the cakes*) Look, Dad.
Mr Peters Yes, very impressive. I just want to check over those sparking plugs and top up the water before we go.
Sue Not in your new blazer, Dad—you'll get oil all over it.
Mr Peters Good thinking. (*He peels off his blazer and boater and hangs them on the rail of the caravan steps*) Back in a jiffy.

No. 5B. Morris Dance II

The morris dancers cross over again as Mr Peters goes off

Worzel, peering craftily round the back of the caravan, checks that the coast is clear, then approaches the children

Worzel Oy! Why for is all them folk goin' backwards an' forrards an' forrards an' backwards an' upsy and dupsy an' this way an' that way and prancin' and dancin' and mincin' an' mince pies.

During the following Worzel tries to remove butterfly buns from Sue's basket and she slaps his hand away each time

Sue No. Worzel.

John (*pointing to the banners*) Worzel—even *you* must know what day it is.

Worzel Ar. I've seen that writin' afore—but I can't make end nor tail of it. I can't find my readin' 'ead see—I reckons the pigs must've eaten it. (*Trying to read*) "Egalliv efte".

Sue Egalliv efte? Is that scarecrow language?

John 'Course it isn't. It's village fête read backwards.

Worzel Village fête, eh? That means my intended'll be there, 'avin' wooden balls chucked at 'er 'ead.

Sue You mean Mr Shepherd's Aunt Sally? Are you going to marry her?

Worzel She's considerin' it very careful but she can't abide my clothes.

John I'm not surprised. You look as if you'd been dragged through a hedge backwards and you pong!

Worzel It jus' so 'appens I *'as* been dragged through an 'edge backwards— by that there bull down at Foggy Bottom. An' you'd pong too if you'd been dragged through a smelly cowpat. (*Craftily; fingering Mr Peters' blazer*) My, my, my, that there's a nice jacket. In fack—that's a jacket an' an 'arf, that there is!

Sue Worzel, *no!*

John Anyway—*you* can't go to the fête. You've got to stay in Ten Acre Field and scare crows.

Worzel T'aint fair, having to scare crows on your birthday.

John It was your birthday last week.

Worzel That was a different birthday. Us scarecrows 'as more birthdays than you yewmans does. We 'as birthdays for our arms an' legs an' one fer our stumick—which is what mine is today. An' them there dratted crows means to spoil it! Juss' look at all them varmints on yon farmhouse roof— 'undreds an' millions of 'em—just waitin' to spoil ol' Worzel's birthday.

John }
Sue } (*together*) Where?

Worzel Up there. Have you gone knock-eyed or something?

John I can't see anything.

As the children look towards the farmhouse, Worzel snatches the blazer and boater and darts off with them

Sue Worzel! Come back with that blazer!

No. 5C. Hurry Music

John and Sue give chase as the morris dancers cross over again

Mrs Braithwaite, ready to leave for the fête, emerges from the farmhouse

Mrs Braithwaite (*calling back into the house to Mr Braithwaite*) Come along, Jack, do! I'm beginning to think you don't want to go to that fête at all!

Mr Braithwaite comes out looking most uncomfortable in a serge suit, tight collar and bowler hat

Mr Braithwaite How did you guess that? If it were left to me I'd sooner spend the afternoon mucking out the pigs.

Mrs Braithwaite Yes, well it isn't left to you, so you can look as if you're enjoying yourself even if you aren't.

Mr Braithwaite Here comes Mrs Bloomsbury-Barton. Don't give her anything else for that tea-tent.

Mrs Braithwaite I certainly won't. She's got a day's baking and two dozen eggs out of me already!

Mrs Braithwaite switches on a false smile as Mrs Bloomsbury-Barton, the Lady of the Manor, sweeps into view, rehearsing her speech for the opening of the fête

Mrs Bloomsbury-Barton Quite unaccustomed as I am to public speaking, may I say that standing here today ... Oh! Mr and Mrs Braithwaite! I was just rehearsing my brief opening remarks from the platform ... I do hope you don't mind my taking a short cut through your land.

Mr Braithwaite Not a bit—but you won't get that Rolls Royce of yours through my cowshed without scratching, Mrs Bloomsbury-Barton.

Mrs Bloomsbury-Barton I've sent the car on ahead to wait for me at the crossroads, Mr Braithwaite. On important public occasions such as this, one does like a few solitary moments in lea and meadow to collect one's thoughts, you know ... (*Resuming her speech*) Quite unaccustomed as I am ...

Mrs Bloomsbury-Barton drifts out of sight and out of earshot

Mr Braithwaite Come on, before she takes fright of the dog and comes back ...

The Braithwaites, heading for the fête, go off. Immediately the shirtsleeved Mr Peters, with Sue and John in tow, enter from the opposite direction, heading for the caravan

Mr Peters I don't understand the pair of you! How can a tramp walk into a private farmyard in broad daylight and waltz off with a brand-new blazer?

John But he did! Look! (*He points to the empty rail where Mr Peters left the blazer*)

During the following, Sue nips into the caravan and emerges with her father's old sports jacket

Mr Peters Couldn't you have stopped him?

John What—have a go, do you mean? He was a very big tramp, Dad.

Mr Peters Hm. Well, maybe you're right. But you should have called for help.

Sue Never mind, Dad—now you can wear your favourite old sports coat.

Mr Peters (*grumbling as they move off*) That's all very well, Sue—I paid a lot of money for that blazer . . .

John \
Sue } (*together*) Oh come on, Dad.

Mr Peters and the children move off

We hear the sound of a dog barking

Mrs Bloomsbury-Barton hurries back into the farmyard. As she speaks, Worzel, wearing the purloined boater and blazer, enters the farmyard over the stile and stands in front of Mrs Bloomsbury-Barton with his arms outstretched in the regulation scarecrow position

Mrs Bloomsbury-Barton Stop that at once! Don't you bare your teeth at me, or I shall report you to Mr Braithwaite! Back into your kennel, sir! (*She sees Worzel*) EEK!

Worzel Good-mornin', missus.

Mrs Bloomsbury-Barton (*very nervously*) I'm sorry, my man—I've no change.

Worzel Ar, now I's glad you mentioned change, missus. I's glad you brought that subjeck up. 'Ow would you like to change places with me?

Mrs Bloomsbury-Barton backs away. She is about to retreat the way she came but the dog barking compels her to change her mind

Mrs Bloomsbury-Barton Stand aside, please.

Worzel Not for ever, mind. Just till tea-time. 'Cos I could do with an arternoon off, see——

Mrs Bloomsbury-Barton Minster, my chauffeur, is only at the end of the lane, you know. I have but to call him.

Worzel You'd make a fine scarecrow, so you would, missus. You just stand in the middle of Ten Acre Field an' you'd scare every rook from 'ere to Foggy Bottom. Ar!

Mrs Bloomsbury-Barton (*calling*) Minster! Minster!

Worzel Ar, now let me give you a bit of advice. You won't scare rooks by shouting Mint Sauce at 'em. Sheep yes, rooks no.

Mrs Bloomsbury-Barton My man, if you don't cease this nonsense at once I shall fetch a policeman.

Worzel Policeman's no good for this job, missus. Too 'ansome. You needs to be ugly, see. Like you an' me. With a big ugly 'at, like what you're wearin'.

Mrs Bloomsbury-Barton How dare you be so offensive!

Worzel Now what's wrong with me 'aving an arternoon off, I'd like to know?

Mrs Bloomsbury-Barton For the last time—will you please let me pass?

Worzel I'll let 'ee pass when I gets a civil answer to a civil question! I'm axin' 'ee, nice an' perlite, will 'ee or won't 'ee be a scarecrow for the arternoon? All you got to do is 'old your arms out, see, like this 'ere . . .

Worzel grabs Mrs Bloomsbury-Barton's arms and pulls them wide on either side of her. She panics and starts to run off

Mrs Bloomsbury-Barton (*screaming*) Help! Police! Minster! Murder! Help!

She departs, with the sound of an angry dog contributing to the noise

Worzel (*genuinely puzzled*) Well I'll be flopaluted! What a funny woman! She must be barmy to take on so! An' now I's got nobody to scare crows for me. An' I shan't get to that there Llivage Efte. An' I shan't see my Aunt Sally in my nice new clothes to axe 'er to marry me, an' we shan't live for ever on cups o' tea an' slices o' cake. I don't suppose she'd say "yes" anyways—even if I 'ad a cup o' tea an' a slice o' cake to offer 'er. She could marry anybody she wanted in the whole wide world. So why should she put up with a good-fer-nuthin' like me . . .? (*He sings*)

No. 6. Why Should She Choose A Scarecrow?

Why should she choose a scarecrow?
What have I got to give her?
How can this thing
Made of straw and of string
Set Aunt Sally's heart a-quiver?
Why should she want to want me?
How can I win her favour?
And how do I tell her
This smelly old feller
Would lay down his life to save her?
When will she learn I love her?
How can I make her hear me?
Would it be best
If I wore a clean vest—
Would she come just a little bit near me?
How can I live without her?
What kind of life would that be?
Not much good, I suppose,
On my own scaring crows
Instead of her caring for me . . .

Despondently, Worzel hangs his head at the end of the song as the rooks caw angrily overhead. He arrives at a decision

(*Speaking*) Bloomin' rooks, cawin' an' cacklin'! I shall go to that there Llivage Efte, whether or no!

And off he marches over the stile

The rooks' chorus grows to a climax and then dies away

SCENE 7

The Village Fête

No. 6A. Morris Dance III

The morris dancers take us into the village fête where their dance reaches its climax

The vicar, watched by the morris dancers and villagers including the Braith-waites, Mr Peters, John and Sue, PC Parsons and Miss Lewisham, introduces Mrs Bloomsbury-Barton

Vicar And now, without further ado, I would ask Mrs Bloomsbury-Barton to be so gracious as to declare our village fête open.

Mrs Bloomsbury-Barton, with a sheaf of notes, mounts the rostrum to lukewarm applause

During the following, Mr Shepherd arrives with Aunt Sally in a handcart. Stiff and lifeless, she is lying in such a position that only her legs are visible. He dumps her at the side of the tea-tent and joins the crowd around Mrs Bloomsbury-Barton

Mrs Bloomsbury-Barton Thank you. Unaccustomed as I am to public speaking, I must just utter a few words of thanks to those of our worthy toilers who were not mentioned by our dear vicar. Flowers. The floral display, from Bloomsbury-Barton Hall, was kindly grown by my gar-dener, Mr Micklethwaite. Cakes. The iced cake which is the centre piece of our tea tent was kindly baked by my cook, Mrs Trampleasure, from Bloomsbury-Barton Hall.

Mrs Braithwaite I hope my butterfly buns get a mention.

Mrs Bloomsbury-Barton Sideshows. The skittles alley was kindly con-structed by Mr Wellbeloved, my odd job man, from Bloomsbury-Barton Hall.

Mr Shepherd Sideshows, did she say? How about a word for my Aunt Sally, then?

Mrs Braithwaite She's not had a word for my butterfly buns yet.

Mr Shepherd is approached by Miss Lewisham, the antiques dealer

Miss Lewisham Mr Shepherd. Miss Lewisham of Lewisham Antiques—my card.

During the following, Worzel, wearing Mr Peters' blazer and boater, strolls into the crowd

Mrs Bloomsbury-Barton Miss Lewisham! Mr Shepherd! This is hardly the place to talk business! This is a charity affair. Refreshments. The bottle of gooseberry wine was kindly donated by—— (*Seeing Worzel*) EEEEEEEEEK! (*Dramatically pointing at Worzel*) Officer! Arrest that man!

PC Parsons I know him! He assaulted me!
Mr Peters That's my blazer—grab him!

During the following chase-sequence song, Worzel is pursued hither and thither

No. 7. Chase Him (Version I)

Crowd	Chase him!
	Erase him!
	The ruffian must be caught!
	Before he swipes another hat,
	Before he kicks another cat,
	Before he makes your tyres flat,
	In short
	A lesson he must be taught,
	The ruffian must be caught.
	Scrag him!
	Debag him!
	The scallywag must be got!
	He's made the ladies swoon and faint,
	He'll daub your blooming house with paint,
	He'd try the patience of a saint,
	God wot—
	A paragon he is not,
	The scallywag should be shot!
Boys	No cake or pie remains intact,
Girls	No apple tree goes unattacked,
Mr Braithwaite	The varmint must be slightly cracked,
Vicar	How can we spoil his little act?
Mr Peters	It's not as if for clues we lacked,
Mrs Bloomsbury-	
Barton	That PC Parsons should be sacked,
3rd Man	The villain must be caught and thwacked,
2nd Woman	He's tried our patience, that's a fact,
Crowd	But now rough justice we'll exact and so—
	But which way did he go?
(Speaking)	This way!
	What way?
	That way!
	Which way?
	Not that way!
	Not what way?
	Not this way!
	Not which way?
	This way
	That way

(*Singing*)   What way?
                          There he goes!

                          Catch him!
                          Despatch him!
                          The vagabond must be found!
                          Just wait until we find the place,
                          In which he's hiding from the chase,
                          Just wait until he shows his face around—
                          We'll dig him into the ground,
                          We'll roast him until he's browned,
                          We'll duck him until he's drowned.
                          That vagabond
                               Scallywag
                                  Ruffian
                                     Hooligan
                                        Must be found!

Finally, Worzel comes across a bell-rope swung towards him by the children

John ⎱
Sue   ⎰ (*together*) Get hold of the rope, Worzel!

As the children pull on one end of the rope, Worzel shoots up into the air on the other

  The crowd dashes past

The children lower Worzel again

  John and Sue run off

Worzel spots Aunt Sally's legs sticking out of Mr Shepherd's handcart and hears her sobbing

Worzel 'Ello! I'd know them legs anywhere! That's my Aunt Sally! (*Peering into the handcart*) What a lovely song.

Aunt Sally I'm not singing, I'm wheeping!

Worzel What you doin' down there, Aunt Sally? Why ain't you at the egallvi efte 'avin' wooden balls chucked at your 'ead?

Aunt Sally Stop asking stupid questions, you stupid scarecrow, and help me up!

Worzel All right then. Up-se-daisy, down-se-daisy, then. My, my, ain't your face red—you looks just like a tomato.

Aunt Sally How dare you!

Worzel A nice tomato mind, a prize tomato, that is. Not a shrivelled-up tomato with white fly.

Aunt Sally (*sobbing*) Stop going on about tomatoes!

Worzel 'Ere—what you wheepin' an' blubberin' for, Aunt Sally?

Aunt Sally Never you mind. (*She sobs*) 'Ave you got such a thing as a delicate lace 'anky about your person?

Worzel No I ain't, but you can 'ave a loan of my robin redbreast if you likes, but do leave off that wheepin' an' blubberin', Aunt Sally, I beg of you. (*He gives her the robin*)

Aunt Sally (*sobbing*) Why should I?

Worzel (*sobbing*) 'Cos you'll start *me* off wheepin' an' blubberin', that's why! 'Ere, give me that robin redbreast back!

Aunt Sally Oh! Take it, you miserable turnip, and leave me to my troubles!

Worzel (*soothingly*) Ar—you ain't got no troubles, m'dear. T'aint too bad 'aving wooden balls chucked at your 'ead—I've 'ad 'alf bricks chucked at my 'ead afore now, it never did *me* no 'arm.

Aunt Sally For your instigation, I'm not in the least concerned about having wooden balls chucked at my 'ead. I *happen* to have had wooden balls chucked at my 'ead by lords and dukes.

Worzel Then what was you wheepin' an' blubberin' for?

Aunt Sally Because the man what owns me wants to sell me and I'll probably be sent to Americky.

Worzel Don't 'ee want to go to Americky, then?

Aunt Sally What—and 'ave to marry a common fillum star?

Worzel You don't 'as to marry no fillum things, Aunt Sally. You could marry ol' Worzel—an' live in his barn 'appily ever after.

Aunt Sally Don't be absurd.

Worzel Why for absurd?

Aunt Sally Because you're ugly and stupid and smelly, that's why!

Worzel Everybody knows that—but give me a proper reason.

Aunt Sally Well, you're common. You have no *breeding*. If you'd lived with the Romanies, like what *I* have done, they'd 'ave chucked you on the bonfire right quick.

Worzel (*cowering in alarm*) Don't say that word, Aunt Sally, don't ever say b-b-b-b-bonfire in front of a scarecrow, not never!

Aunt Sally Bonfire!

Worzel Now you stop that, Aunt Sally!

Aunt Sally Big—burning—bonfire!

Worzel I shall tell the Crowman!

Aunt Sally See if *I* care . . . *I* know where there's a box of matches.

Worzel Box of what? You wouldn't! Not to a pure ol' Worzel what's made o' twigs and straw! Mercy, Aunt Sally, mercy!

Aunt Sally Very well, you snivelling haystack. I shall show you mercy if you do something for me in return.

Worzel Anything, Aunt Sally, anything!

Aunt Sally I want you to take my place so I can go off and enjoy myself.

Worzel Take your place—what—an' get wooden balls chucked at my 'ead? No fear.

Aunt Sally No-one's going to chuck wooden balls at your 'ead, silly! All you have to do is sit in this 'ere 'andcart dressed as me.

Worzel What—ol' Worzel dress up in all them women's clothes? Not likely.

Aunt Sally Not even to please me?

Worzel I'd like to please 'ee, Aunt Sally, but I'm not puttin' no frock on! Not even to please you.

Aunt Sally Not even if I was to marry you?

Worzel Marry me? You'd really marry ol' Worzel if 'e changes place with you?

Aunt Sally I might.

Worzel You's made me the 'appiest scarecrow this side o' Foggy Bottom, Aunt Sally. I'll do what you wants—an' then I'll marry you—an' then I'll kick you from 'ere to Michaelmas.

Aunt Sally You wouldn't dare!

Worzel Yes I would.

Aunt Sally You are no gentleman.

Worzel I know I ain't—I's a scarecrow.

Aunt Sally That's right. A stupid, igorant old scarecrow.

Worzel An' you're a wicked, 'eartless piece o' furninture.

Aunt Sally Turnip-face!

Worzel Bundle o' firewood!

Aunt Sally Haystack!

Worzel Broom 'andle!

Aunt Sally Flue brush!

Worzel Coconut shy!

Aunt Sally What did you just call me?

Worzel Coconut shy!

Aunt Sally If I 'adn't been brung up a lady, for that I'd smash you in the face with a cream jam-sponge!

Worzel (*wistfully*) Would you really? I ain't been smashed in the face with a cream jam-sponge fer ages an' ages!

Aunt Sally There's 'undreds an' 'undreds of 'em in the tea-tent.

Worzel Tea-tent? Did you say tea-tent? Can we 'ave cups o' tea an' slices o' cake in there?

Aunt Sally Indeed we can. It ain't open to yewmans yet so we can eat ourselves sick without being disturbed. But you've got to promise after you *have* eaten yourself sick that you'll change places with me.

Worzel Oh, I don't know about that, Aunt Sally.

Aunt Sally Please, Worzel.

Worzel Oh, I don't know about that, Aunt Sally.

Aunt Sally Pretty please.

Worzel Oh, I don't know about that, Aunt Sally.

Aunt Sally I beseech you!

Worzel Dang me, Aunt Sally, you don't 'ave to do no beseechin'.

Aunt Sally Good.

No. 8. Slice of Cake

Worzel (*singing*)	It don't take much to tempt me,
	Don't need no beggin' an' pleadin',
Aunt Sally (*singing*)	Your stumick is allus empty,
	Your face forever needs feedin'
Worzel	If you wants to disarm me, tease me, charm me,
	Command me to do your slavin',

	I'm yours to obey for forever an' a day
	If you'll only remember my cravin'
Aunt Sally	An' after all it don't take a lot
	To stop you gettin' tearful,
Worzel	Just three things—one cold, one 'ot—
	An' both o' 'em keeps me cheerful

Worzel }
Aunt Sally }   A slice o' cake an' a cup of tea

Worzel   Suits Aunt Sally an' that suits me

Worzel }
Aunt Sally }   Offer us the world but all we'll take
                        Is a cup of tea, an' a slice o' cake,
                        A cup o' tea an' a slice o' cake,
                        When the moon comes up or at daybreak,
                        Ever after we'll live happilee—
                        On slices o' cake an' cups o' tea.

*Towards the end of the chorus Sue and John arrive on the scene. As Worzel
and Aunt Sally disappear into the tea-tent, Sue and John continue the song,
peeping into the tea-tent the while to watch Aunt Sally and Worzel gorging
themselves unseen by the audience*

John }
Sue }   A cup of tea filled to the brim,
                        Suits Aunt Sally so that suits him,
                        They don't want a bottle of fancy wine,
                        Offer them a brewery and they'll decline,
                        A slice of cake, cut it nice and thick,
                        Smother it in icing they can lick, and
                        Ever ever after they'll live happilee

John   On slices of cake,
Sue   On slices of cake,
John   On slices of cake,
Sue   On slices of cake,
Both   On slices of cake,
                        And cups of tea!

At the end of the song John and Sue peer into the tea-tent

John No, Aunt Sally!
Sue Stop it, Worzel!

*They turn round and we see that their faces are covered with cream where
Worzel and Aunt Sally have hurled cakes at them*

Mrs Bloomsbury-Barton sweeps on

Mrs Bloomsbury-Barton Naughty, greedy, children! You've been sampling
the cakes in the tea-tent, haven't you?
Sue No, Mrs Bloomsbury-Barton.
Mrs Bloomsbury-Barton Don't fib to me or I shall tell your father. Go and
wash your faces at once.
Sue Yes, Mrs Bloomsbury-Barton.

Mrs Bloomsbury-Barton And then I want you to scour the fête and find Mr Shepherd. I'm loking for him most urgently.

John Yes, Mrs Bloomsbury-Barton.

Mrs Bloomsbury-Barton Well, off you go ... Oh dear me, so much to organize.

As the children run off and Mrs Bloomsbury-Barton dithers on her way, Miss Lewisham and Mr Shepherd stroll on

Miss Lewisham ... if it's a *genuine* Aunt Sally, Mr Shepherd, then I can offer you a very good price.

Mr Shepherd Oh, it's genuine all right. Came from a travelling fair, it did, over a hundred years ago.

Miss Lewisham Mark you, it would have to be in good condition.

Mr Shepherd Wait till you see it, Miss Lewisham. I've taken really good care of that Aunt Sally.

Mr Peters joins them

Mr Peters There you are, Mr Shepherd. Mrs Bloomsbury-Barton's on the warpath. She wants to know when you're going to get that Aunt Sally up so we can start throwing coconuts at it.

Mr Shepherd You don't throw coconuts, Mr Peters, you *win* coconuts. What you throw is wooden balls.

Mr Peters Wooden balls, then. Shall I give you a hand with it?

Mr Shepherd Mr Peters, chucking wooden balls at my Aunt Sally would be like chucking wooden balls at a Sheraton sideboard. It's a valuable antique, man! Here we are, Miss Lewisham ...

He directs her over to the empty handcart

Miss Lewisham Where?

Mr Shepherd It's not there!

Miss Lewisham I can see that!

Mr Shepherd You know what's happened, don't you? That Mrs Bloomsbury-Barton's had it set up without so much as a by-your-leave! Just wait till I see her ...

Mr Peters They'll be chucking coconuts at it by now.

Mr Shepherd Wooden balls!

Miss Lewisham I do hope not. It'll chip the paint.

As the three of them hurry off, Aunt Sally comes out of the tea-tent, wearing Worzel's clothes. She is fascinated by the sight of her trousered legs—they have always been concealed from her under her dress before—and displays them to herself admiringly

Aunt Sally Coo! Just fancy! What an 'andsome pair of legs. I will never cover them with a frock again. My my my, ain't they just the ticket!

No. 9. Aunt Sally's Dance

The Chaplinesque postures with which she has been experimenting lead her into a little dance in which she eccentrically shows off her legs' paces

At the end of this, Worzel comes out of the tea-tent dressed incongruously as Aunt Sally, and wiping his mouth

Worzel That was the finest tea I's ever eaten since I got made, Aunt Sally. But I don't 'alf look a right ol' fool in these 'ere womeny knickers.

Aunt Sally No more of a fool than you looked already. How do *I* look?

Worzel Like a real Romany tink, Aunt Sally, like a real Romany tink.

Aunt Sally Thank you. Now all you have to do is get in that there handcart and keep your stupid trap shut.

Worzel You promises me that nobody's going to chuck no wooden balls at my 'ead?

Aunt Sally You have my word.

Worzel An' I 'as your word that when this is all over, you'll give me that little wooden 'and o' yourn in marriage?

Aunt Sally gives Worzel a mighty shove that lands him in the handcart with his legs in the air, just as he found her earlier. He stays in that position during the following scene

Aunt Sally Of course. *Unless* it so happens that you've been nailed down in a crate and shipped to Americky. Toodle-oo!

No. 9A. Music Link

Aunt Sally struts off. Mr Shepherd, Miss Lewisham and Mr Peters return

Mr Shepherd I don't understand it. If Mrs Bloomsbury-Barton hasn't got my Aunt Sally, who has?

Miss Lewisham I really don't know, Mr Shepherd, but I'm beginning to think I'm wasting my time.

Mr Shepherd You wait till you see it, Miss Lewisham. You'll call it time—and money—well spent.

They arrive at the handcart where Miss Lewisham examines Worzel's legs protruding

Mr Peters Well I'll be blowed! It's turned up again.

Mr Shepherd There you are, Miss Lewisham. Is that a valuable antique or isn't it?

Miss Lewisham That thing? An antique Aunt Sally? It looks more like a Guy Fawkes left over from bonfire night!

Mr Shepherd Wait a minute—that's not my Aunt Sally? That's a mangel worzel, that is!

Miss Lewisham I'm afraid you've brought me round here on a fool's errand, Mr Shepherd.

Mr Shepherd Aren't you going to make me an offer, then?

Miss Lewisham Certainly. How about tuppence?

She sweeps off

Mr Shepherd I've never been so insulted in all my life. Blooming thing! I might as well chuck it on the bonfire now.

Mr Peters Not till after the fête, Mr Shepherd. It's still an Aunt Sally, after a fashion—why not let the kids chuck a few coconuts at it?

Mr Shepherd Wooden balls, Mr Peters! They *win* a coconut if they knock its head off. And that shouldn't take much doing, by the look of it.

No. 9B. Music Link

Together, Mr Shepherd and Mr Peters wheel the "Aunt Sally" across to the coconut shy pitch. Worzel, lolling out of the handcart, looks horror-struck

To you from me, Mr Peters . . .

Mr Peters and Mr Shepherd get the "Aunt Sally" into position

During the following, several villagers, including Mrs Bloomsbury-Barton and Mr and Mrs Braithwaite, circulate among the sideshows

Mr Peters Careful with its head, Mr Shepherd—it's loose. It'll come off if you knock it about like that.

Mr Shepherd It needs to come off—it's the ugliest thing I've ever seen. I'd like to know what's happened to my antique Aunt Sally.

Mr Peters It'll turn up, Mr Shepherd. They always do in the end, stolen goods. Unless of course she's been chopped up for firewood.

Mrs Bloomsbury-Barton approaches

Mrs Bloomsbury-Barton Ah, Mr Shepherd . . . Good gracious, what an ugly Aunt Sally! However, I've promised to have one turn at every attraction in the fête. Shall I, so to speak, set the ball rolling?

Mr Shepherd All the same to me, Mrs Bloomsbury-Barton.

Mrs Bloomsbury-Barton picks up a wooden ball and takes aim

Mrs Bloomsbury-Barton I declare this coconut shy well and truly open! (*She throws and misses*)

Mr Shepherd (*pointedly*) Like another go, Mrs Bloomsbury-Barton? Five balls for tenpence?

Mrs Bloomsbury-Barton No thank you, Mr Shepherd. Time to open the tea-tent—I promised the vicar I would cut the first slice of cake.

Mrs Bloomsbury-Barton moves off and enters the tea-tent during the following

Mr Peters Come on now! Roll up for the Aunt Sally! Knock her head off with a coconut!

Mr Shepherd Come along now! Test your skill! Five balls for tenpence! How about you, Mr Braithwaite?

Mr Braithwaite That's a horrible-looking Aunt Sally, Mr Shepherd!

He takes aim. But before he can throw there is an ear-piercing shriek from inside the tea-tent

Mrs Bloomsbury-Barton rushes out

Mrs Bloomsbury-Barton Police Constable Parsons! Mr Braithwaite! Mr Shepherd! Everyone! Come quickly! The tea-tent's been raided!

PC Parsons Raided?

Mrs Bloomsbury-Barton Yes—look! (*She pulls back the tent flap to reveal a scene of devastation*)

Mrs Braithwaite My poor butterfly buns!

Mrs Bloomsbury-Barton Never mind your butterfly buns! What about Mrs Trampleasure's iced cake from Bloomsbury-Barton Hall! All over the tent!

PC Parsons It's that tramp again.

Mr Braithwaite We'll get him this time.

Mr Peters Follow me!

No. 9C. Chase Him (Instrumental Reprise)

The crowd go off in pursuit of Worzel

Aunt Sally comes along munching candy-floss. She espies Worzel in the coconut shy

Aunt Sally My goodness! And what have we here! A coconut shy! What a common-looking Aunt Sally!

Worzel It ain't an Aunt Sally, Aunt Sally, it's me! An' you can 'ave your clothes back now, 'cos that woman don't want to buy you an' send you to Americky after all.

Aunt Sally How most peculiar! I almost thought I heard that ugly old hobject talking!

Worzel You did, Aunt Sally. It's Worzel—what's going to marry you!

Aunt Sally It must be the wind blowing through its ugly turnip head. I know what I'll do—I'll chuck a few coconuts at it—that'll stop him.

Worzel Not coconuts, Aunt Sally! You chuck wooden balls.

Aunt Sally Oh, but I promised you wouldn't have wooden balls chucked at you—and I always keep my word. So cop a coconut!

She throws a coconut, but it goes wide of the mark. It sails through the air

Worzel Missed me! Nyah nyah nyah——

Both Worzel and Aunt Sally freeze in horror as there is an almighty sound of smashing glass

That's done it! Run for it, Aunt Sally!

Picking up his skirts, Worzel hares off, accompanied by Aunt Sally. A furious Mrs Bloomsbury-Barton hurries into view, with the crowd following

Mrs Bloomsbury-Barton Where is he, where is he, where is he! Where's the ruffian that broke my Rolls Royce windscreen?

Crowd There he is!

Mr Shepherd There he goes!

PC Parsons After him!

No. 10. Chase Him (Version II)

Crowd	Get him!
	Upset him!
	The hooligan we will thrash!
	Disaster reigns where he has been,
	We hope, again he won't be seen
Mrs Bloomsbury-	Who'll pay to mend my Rolls' windscreen
Barton	In cash?
Crowd	We'll bring him out in a rash!
	The hooligan we will thrash!
	Nobody dare go out at night,
	For fear of what he's done, or might,
	Poor Mr Shepherd's hair's turned white,
Mr Peters	Can no-one help us in our plight,
Crowd	Our constable is not so bright,
	Or is he scared to make a fight?
	That rascal should be locked up tight,
	Not roaming round in broad daylight,
	We think he's doing it for spite,
	And how!
	But whereabouts is he now?
(Speaking)	This way!
	What way?
	That way!
	Which way?
	Not that way!
	Not what way?
	Not this way!
	Not which way?
	Which way?
	Which way?
	Which way?
(Singing)	There he goes!
	Catch him!
	Despatch him!
	The vagabond must be found!
	Just wait until we find the place,
	In which he's hiding from the chase,
	Just wait until he shows his face
	around—
	We'll dig him into the ground,
	We'll roast him until he's browned,
	We'll duck him until he's drowned.
	That vagabond
	Scallywag
	Ruffian
	Hooligan must be found!

As the crowd move off and the fête set is struck, the Crowman hurries on anxiously, carrying a battered old telescope

Crowman Sergeant Beetroot! Come along, Sergeant, hurry!

Sergeant Beetroot, a scruffy military scarecrow with a scarlet face and enormous shapeless army greatcoat, marches on. Straw scatters from his sleeve as he salutes

Beetroot Sergeant Beetroot! First Scarecrow Life Guards, reporting, sah!

Crowman (*peering through the telescope*) Yes, come here, Sergeant.

Beetroot Sorry to be late on parade, sah—my old combine-'arvester wound's giving me gyp.

The Crowman hands Sergeant Beetroot the telescope

Crowman My eyes aren't what they were—has he given them the slip?

Beetroot looks through the telescope the wrong way

What can you see?

Beetroot Dunno, sir. Everything's gone all small.

Crowman Other way round, Sergeant Beetroot.

Beetroot Beg to report, no sign of either Scarecrow Gummidge nor the carved wooden female figure Aunt Sally.

Crowman Thank heavens for that, because you know what they'd do to him if they caught him, Sergeant Beetroot?

Beetroot Tear 'im to bits, I shouldn't wonder, sah—'im being made only of straw.

Crowman And when they found he *was* only made of straw, Sergeant, what then? What of all the other scarecrows walking the earth? Replaced by electric crowscarers, every man jack of them.

Beetroot Sah, it don't bear thinkin' about.

Crowman Exactly. Sergeant Beetroot, I have a special mission for you.

Beetroot For you, sir, my creator, no mission too dangerous or impossible, sah!

Crowman This one is neither dangerous or impossible.

Beetroot Sah.

Crowman I want you to follow Worzel and see that he keeps out of mischief.

Beetroot It's a bit of a dark outlook for following.

Crowman It'll be an even darker outlook for Worzel if he doesn't behave— Sergeant Beetroot, dismissed.

Sergeant Beetroot salutes as he and the Crowman go off their separate ways

SCENE 8

Scatterbrook Farm and Barn

No. 10A. Music Link

Worzel and Aunt Sally, now wearing their own clothes again, cross Ten Acre on their way to the barn. They are eating apples which they toss over their shoulders after taking a bite or two

Worzel That was a very nice eleventy-twelve apples, that was. 'Ave 'ee got stumick ache, Aunt Sally, 'cos I 'as?

Aunt Sally Don't be vulgar. Ladies don't 'ave stumicks.

Worzel (*as they enter the barn*) Well—'ere we are, Aunt Sally.

Aunt Sally What do you mean—'ere we are?

Worzel My little 'ome where me an' you's going to live 'appily 'appily after—when we's married.

Aunt Sally *This* place? You expect me, a genuine mahogany Aunt Sally, to live *here*?

Worzel Why, what's wrong with it? (*He sings*)

No. 11. It'll Suit Us

        It'll suit us,
        It'll do us to a "T"—
        It'll suit us,
        An' what's more it comes rent free!
        It's as cute as,
        Just as cute as cute can be—
        An' it'll suit us.

Aunt Sally It's a hovel,
        It's an awful dirty mess!
        It's a hovel,
        It's not my kind of address!
        You can grovel
        But at best you must confess—
        That it's a hovel.

Worzel We'll be 'appy,
        If it's rainin' 'ard outside—
        We'll be 'appy,
        Couldn't be 'appier if we tried.
        Make it snappy,
        Settle down an' be my bride—
        An' make me 'appy.

Aunt Sally It's so sordid,
        It's the wrong side of the tracks!
        It's so sordid,
        Everything I need it lacks!
        It's so morbid,
        I could smash it with an axe—
        'Cos it's so sordid.

Worzel	It's a fine place,
	An' it's better than the rest—
	It's a fine place,
	Even better than up west,
	A divine place,
	You can't do better than the best—
	'Cos it's a fine place.
Aunt Sally	It's so awful,
	It's completely unrefined,
	It's so awful,
	It's not fit for human kind,
	It's unlawful,
	And there's a smell I've not defined—
	That is so awful.
Worzel	All it needs is a carpet and a curtain.
	It just so happens that I forgot 'em,
	All it needs is you an' then for certain,
	I'd be the 'appiest scarecrow from 'ere to foggy bottom.
Aunt Sally	All it needs is determination
	If I lived here I'd burn it to the ground
	All it needs is a conflagration
	There'd be the biggest bonfire for miles around!

Aunt Sally laughs evilly

Worzel (*speaking*) No, no, no! Besides, you wouldn't do nuthin' like that to this ol' barn, 'cos: (*he sings*)

	It's a great home,
	It's a stately home what's more.
Aunt Sally	It's a hate home,
	I wouldn't deign to cross the floor.
Worzel	A sedate home,
Aunt Sally	It hasn't got a proper door.
Worzel	But it's a great home,
	It's a dream home
Aunt Sally	It's a nightmare home I fear,
Worzel	It's a dream home.
Aunt Sally	I couldn't possibly live here.
Worzel	A supreme home,
Aunt Sally	Not for me—no blinkin' fear!
Worzel	But it's a great home.

Aunt Sally (*speaking*) Hovel.

Worzel Bestest 'ome you'll ever see!

Aunt Sally It smells like a pigsty.

Worzel No, it don't, Aunt Sally—a cowshed maybe, on account of the fact that it's next door to a cowshed. But it don't smell like a pigsty at all. It's me that smells like a pigsty.

Aunt Sally Disgusting!

They are about to start throwing clods at each other

Sue hurries into the barn

Sue There you are, Worzel. Mr Shepherd's looking for you and he's *furious!*

Worzel What's *'e* want with a scarecrow? 'E ain't got a garding big enough for a sparrer to get its breakfast in, never mind a girt flock o' rooks.

Sue You were seen with Aunt Sally in Mrs Bloomsbury-Barton's orchard. Mr Shepherd thinks you're a tramp who's stolen her and he's going to have you locked up! And the Crowman's looking for you!

Worzel The Crowman! Oo-er, that wouldn't suit ol' Worzel. I'd best get back to Ten Acre where I's safe. You wait 'ere, Aunt Sally. Make yourself nice an' comfy an' if you wants to brush your 'air you can use my bestest 'edge'og. (*He hands her the hedgehog*) Coming, Mr Crowman.

Worzel hurries over the stile and reappears in Ten Acre, where he takes up his position on the scarecrow pole

Sue If I were you, Aunt Sally, I'd hide under that pile of straw until Mr Shepherd's gone.

Aunt Sally What—an' mess up my pretty 'ead of 'air? Don't be prepospospos, little girl. Go on—buzz off.

Sue Don't say I didn't warn you!

Sue goes off

Aunt Sally begins brushing her hair with the hedgehog Worzel has given her

Mr Shepherd and Mr Braithwaite appear and head for the barn, pursued by an agitated Crowman

Aunt Sally abruptly breaks off brushing her hair and, setting her limbs rigidly, she is a wooden Aunt Sally again

Mr Braithwaite Mr Shepherd—believe me, I *know* these tinks. A barn next door to a farmhouse is the last place a tramp would head for.

Mr Shepherd We've looked everywhere else, we might just as well make double-sure he's moved on. (*He points triumphantly at Aunt Sally*) Ah! Last place a tramp would come to, eh?

Mr Braithwaite He's not here now though, Mr Shepherd. The bird has flown. But why has he left that thing behind, after going to all the trouble of pinching it in the first place?

Mr Shepherd Realized he couldn't sell it, of course. Who's going to buy a valuable antique Aunt Sally off a tramp?

Mr Braithwaite Well now, you've found it again, Mr Shepherd, I hope you don't want to leave it in my barn—because I've had enough of tramps and Aunt Sallies for one day, thank you very much.

Mr Shepherd It goes back in my attic, Mr Braithwaite, under lock and key. Can I borrow that there skip? (*He points to a dusty old skip stored in the barn*)

During the following, Mr Shepherd and Mr Braithwaite lift up Aunt Sally and put her in the skip and close the lid

Mr Braithwaite You can have it, for all I care. It's no use to me.

Mr Shepherd To you from me.... There we are. Now if we can just carry it out into your yard ... To you from me ...

They carry the skip out into the farmyard

Right. Much obliged. I suppose your tractor's tied up at the present moment?

Mr Braithwaite You suppose right.

Mr Shepherd I'll just pop home and fetch my lorry, then. Will it be all right, d'you think?

Mr Braithwaite I'll keep an eye on it from that window while I have my supper. If that tramp comes back he'll get a backside full of buckshot.

No 11A. Music Link—Sting

Mr Shepherd and Mr Braithwaite go their separate ways

The Crowman comes out of the barn into the farmyard and goes down to the edge of Ten Acre Field

Crowman (*calling*) Worzel! Worzel Gummidge, come here!

Worzel I's scaring crows just at present, Mr Crowman your effervescence, sir.

Crowman Come here, Worzel!

Worzel It's more than my job's worth, your plumptitude, sir.

Crowman Worzel, I said come here.

Worzel Is that an order, Mr Crowman? (*He reluctantly comes forward*)

Crowman It's an order ... I hope you're satisfied with your work. Where have you been? Why weren't you on duty?

Worzel I can explanate all that, your angriness. See, I was on duty, sir, when I saw this bloomin' great crow, Mr Crowman, sir. Bigger nor a sheep, bigger nor a bull, an' I chased it an' chased it all the way to the village——

Crowman Worzel!

Worzel When 'oo should I bump into but Aunt Sally——

Crowman Worzel!

Worzel —what 'as very kindly offered me 'er 'and in marriage, and she's in the barn waitin' for me to finish my day's work.

Crowman Worzel, Aunt Sally isn't in the barn, and she isn't going to marry you.

Worzel Begging your pardon for contradicting your plumptitude, but she is, an' she is.

Crowman Worzel, Aunt Sally is in a basket and she's going back to Mr Shepherd's attic.

Worzel That cold old hattic? Why for, your magnificence?

Crowman Because that's where she belongs.

Worzel If Aunt Sally belongs in a cold old attic then Worzel belongs in a mucky old ditch.

Crowman Worzel, Worzel,—Aunt Sally needs to be in her attic because it's where she dreams her dreams of Egypt and Rumania and marrying a duke and riding in a golden coach. She wouldn't find those things in the cruel world, you know.

Worzel She found me though, didn't she? She found ol' Worzel.

Crowman She did indeed, Worzel. But you're a scarecrow, not a duke. In that stupid wooden head of hers there's a whole magic kingdom—so let her go and dream her dreams.

Worzel An' what about me, sir? What about poor ol' Worzel?

Crowman Haven't you got a magic kingdom?

Worzel I reckon I 'as, Mr Crowman. When I's guardin' that there Ten Acre Field, I gets to thinkin' and dreamin'. The seasons comes an' goes and them little fledglings grow up into great big rooks—and all that time there's thinkin' bein' thunk inside my 'ead. So even when I's cold an' wet, inside my 'ead it might be summery and when I's hungry, inside my'ead I might be eatin' cake, an' when I's lonely, inside my 'ead I can 'ear my Aunt Sally a-saying all kind of manner of wonderful soppy things to me. Ain't nobody knows what's goin' on in this ol' head o' mine.

Crowman Nobody but you and me, Worzel. Now it's time you were a scarecrow again. Back to work.

Worzel Yes, sir, Mr Crowman, sir. (*He returns sadly to his scarecrow pole*)

He and the Crowman exchange salutes

The Crowman moves off

No. 12. Why Should She Choose A Scarecrow? (Reprise)

(*Singing*) How can I live without her?
What kind of life would that be?
Not much good, I suppose,
On my own scarin' crows
Instead of her caring for me.

CURTAIN

ACT II

Outside the Crowman's House. A hot afternoon

The Crowman lives in a mysterious, rickety wooden building deep in the woods. There is a gate to the backyard which is littered with lifeless scarecrows leaning up against the fence or the side of the house. In one corner stands an antique gas street lamp

No. 13. Music

The Crowman is busy at work, repairing a scarecrow, as Sergeant Beetroot enters from the house, carrying a homing pigeon

Beetroot Sergeant Beetroot reporting—sah!

Crowman Yes, Sergeant Beetroot?

Beetroot Carrier pigeon reporting to base, sah! Time of arrival—(*he indicates the alarm clock he carries slung to his waist*)—when the little hand was here, and the big hand was here.

Crowman Distinctly odd ... not Frère Jaques surely? I'm not expecting a report from the French vineyard scarecrows for several days.

Beetroot No, sah! Not Froggy Jaquer! A trifle more close to 'ome, sah— Albert Henry of Scatterbrook Farm.

Crowman (*taking the pigeon*) I might have guessed. What has Worzel been up to this time? Sssh! Don't tell me here, you stupid bird! We'll take him inside and find out, Sergeant. What a pity—I thought this was going to be the perfect day, too. Not a cloud in sight.

Beetroot Very 'ot, sah! Lovely weather for scarecrows.

The Crowman and Sergeant Beetroot go indoors

The music for No. 14 creeps in behind. One by one, the Scarecrows come to life and start to whistle, then to sing:

No. 14. Scarecrow Day

Scarecrows   It's a scarecrow day,
Feel the sun and smell the new-mown hay.
Its the sorta day you ought-a lie down
And while an hour away.
Scarecrow days—

Days for lazin', sheep for grazin' days.
It's amazin'
How without even tryin'
You close your eyes 'n'
You're dreamin'—
And schemin'—
Of a scarecrow day.
Sky of blue has chased the clouds away.
It's the kinda time you find it's sublime
To close your eyes and say
Ho-hey!
Folks call me crazy,
But I'll go my way,
'Cos I'm goin' nowhere
On a scarecrow day.

As the verse comes to an end, the Scarecrows resume their rigid pose, but the music is held in behind, softly, as:

John and Sue approach the Crowman's house

Sue Are you sure this is where the Crowman lives?
John Of course it is, stupid—look at all the scarecrows.
Sue It's a bit creepy.
John (*scornfully*) Creepy! the middle of summer and a sun like that?

John begins to sing the second verse and is joined by Sue

	Sky's blue and not a cloud in sight
Sue	Sun, too, was never quite so bright.
John	Count-to-five day,
Sue	Ain'tcha glad that you're alive day!
John |	Grass never grew so green at all,
Sue /	Who ever knew grass grew so tall?

Hide and seek days—
Count to ten—
Start again.
Summer-time was never so much fun,
Summer-days spent running in the sun,
Climbing-tree days,
Picking-flowers-fancy-free days,
And tomorrow for sure—
Just as good as before.
It's another one more,
One more,
One more scarecrow's day

After which we go into a counterpoint reprise of the song. The number is choreographed as a spirited dance for the children and the Scarecrows. As the number ends the Scarecrows go back to their rigid positions

No. 14A. Spooky Music Link

Sue What can we tell the Crowman?

John Everything, stupid! About how Worzel's been sulking for days—ever since Mr Shepherd took Aunt Sally away. And how the rooks are eating all the crops in Ten Acre Field because Worzel won't come out of the barn. And how Mr Braithwaite says he's going to get an electric crow-scarer and throw Worzel on the compost heap ...

At the mention of the dreaded word, there is a flutter of anxiety and a worried murmur from the Scarecrows behind the children. John and Sue jump with fright

John What was that?

Sue I don't know but it's getting creepy again! And stop calling me stupid— if anyone's stupid, it's you! You *can't* tell the Crowman about Worzel. We're not supposed to know that Worzel can walk and talk.

A shadow falls across the Crowman's yard as the evening begins to draw in

It's getting creepier every second! I'm going back to Scatterbrook—now! (*She crosses to the gate*) Are you coming with me—or are you going to stay here all on your own?

John glances round, nervously at the Scarecrows. He makes up his mind

John Hang on—I'm coming with you!

The Crowman appears

Crowman Looking for someone, children?

John nods his head as Sue shakes hers

John } (*together*) { Yes!
Sue } { No!

Crowman "Yes"? "No"? Does that mean that one of you is looking for someone and the other one isn't?

This time it is Sue who nods her head while John shakes his

Sue } (*together*) { Yes!
John } { No!

Crowman Dear me! You are in a muddle. Do you want to tell me about it?

John bites his lip and glances at Sue who shakes her head, vehemently. But John takes a deep breath and decides to reveal all

John It's about Worzel Gum——

He is silenced by a sharp kick on the shin from Sue

Ow!

Sue (*taking over; tactfully*) It's about a scarecrow, Mr Crowman.

Crowman That's better.

Sue The one at Scatterbrook Farm—in Ten Acre Field. Do you know the one we mean?

The Crowman sighs heavily

Crowman Yes, I know exactly which one you mean.

Sue We think you ought to come and take a look at him—(*correcting herself*)—it.

John We think if you don't. Farmer Braithwaite might throw him—(*also correcting himself*)—it on the compost heap.

Another uneasy stir and an anxious murmur from the rigid Scarecrows in the yard

Crowman (*silencing the Scarecrows discreetly*) Hush! (*To the children*) Well now—why on earth should Farmer Braithwaite throw a scarecrow on the ... decide to dispose of it? What's wrong with it?

The children exchange a worried glance—unsure to what extent they can commit themselves

Sue He—it doesn't seem to be working properly.

John takes a very deep breath

John We think he's—it's—unhappy.

Crowman Unhappy? What imaginations you children do have! How on earth can he—it—be unhappy? A scarecrow hasn't got feelings!

But the children stand their ground

John All the same, we still think you ought to take a look at it.

Sue Please, Mr Crowman.

Crowman Oh—very well. The next time I'm in the vicinity of Scatterbrook I'll pop into the barn and see if there's anything I can do. Does that satisfy you?

The children nod enthusiastically. They move to leave

John (*turning back*) Mr Crowman?

Crowman Now what is it?

John How did you *know* that Wor——that the scarecrow was in the barn? You haven't been near the farm for weeks.

Crowman A little bird told me. Now be off with you.

The children scamper off

The Crowman's face darkens

Worzel Gummidge—one of these days you'll try my patience just that little bit too far! Sergeant Beetroot!

Sergeant Beetroot comes out of the house and snaps smartly to attention

Beetroot Sah!

Crowman Take note, Sergeant—one more black mark against Worzel Gummidge's name and he'll stand before a jury of his fellow scarecrows!

Beetroot Not a scarecrow trial, yer honour?

Crowman Why not?

Beetroot Why, we h'ain't 'ad one of them for years. Wiv respeck, sah—I don't like 'em, sah—nasty things.

Crowman I'm none too fond of them myself, Sergeant—but if Gummidge doesn't mend his ways he's going to leave me little option.

Beetroot What's he been getting up to this time?

Crowman That's what you should be telling me, Sergeant. I ordered you to keep him out of mischief.

Beetroot Beg to report, sah—was on sick leave with my combine 'arvester wound.

Crowman Rubbish.

Beetroot Left Pigeon Albert Henry on guard duty—sah!

Crowman Yes, well not only have we had Pigeon Albert Henry winging in with news of Worzel's latest disobedience, there've been two children here telling me that in their opinion Worzel is unhappy!

Beetroot *Yewman* children, sah?

Crowman Yes—human children.

Beetroot But how could *yewman* children know the innermost workings of a scarecrow's 'eart, sah? T'ain't possible.

Crowman Indeed it isn't, Sergeant. Why, not even a rogue of Worzel's calibre would let humans know about our secrets ... No, it doesn't bear thinking about.

Beetroot Permission to speak—sah!

Crowman Permission granted, Sergeant.

Beetroot Sah! Wiv respect—sah—regarding the carved wooden female figure known as Aunt Sally—sah!

Crowman Aunt Sally?

Beetroot Well, sah—if Aunt Sally being locked in a trunk is the cause of Scarecrow Gummidge sulking and not doing his work proper—wive respect, sah—he might be better behaved if she was brought back.

Crowman "Brought back", Sergeant?

Beetroot I am a military scarecrow of your creation an' think you know the way my mind works, yer honour.

Crowman Yes, I do.

Beetroot I've been thinking, sah, of a rescue being effected.

Crowman Rescue Aunt Sally? From Mr Shepherd—her rightful owner? What becomes of Aunt Sally, Sergeant, is entirely Aunt Sally's own affair. Why—she isn't even a scarecrow!

Beetroot Granted, yer 'onour. But the scarecrow Gummidge *is* a scarecrow. And if he's to go round blabbing his mouth off, because of his feeling lonely, to yewman kids and so forth ...

Crowman We have no definite proof that he has been, as you succinctly put it, blabbing his mouth off, and I hope for the sake of all scarecrows that he hasn't.

Beetroot Would you put it past him, yer 'ighness?

Crowman (*with a sigh*) I wouldn't put anything past him.

Beetroot My sentiments exactly, sah. Which is why I'm putting forward the idea of rescuing the h'object of 'is 'eart's desire.

Crowman And who are you proposing should take on the task?

Sergeant Beetroot snaps to attention and takes a smart pace forward

Beetroot Prepared to take on the assliniment myself—sah!

Crowman Single-handed, Sergeant?

Beetroot No, sah! Wiv the assistance of Scarecrow Gummidge 'imself, sah. A spot o' frontline dooty might serve to snap 'im out of 'imself. An' also, wiv your 'onour's permission, I should also like to take a couple of my other lads along as well also wiv me. (*He turns and bellows across the yard*) Soggy Boggart!

The Scarecrow referred to comes to life and snaps to attention

Soggy S'arnt!

Beetroot Scabby Tater-Blight!

A second Scarecrow, a diminutive one with a piping voice, also comes to life

Scabby Did you want me, Sergeant Beetroot?

Beetroot You've been summoned, Scabby, by the call o' dooty. You two likely lads is to come along o' me.

Soggy What's it all about, S'arnt?

Sergeant Beetroot hands out "arms"—a hoe and a rake. He selects a pitchfork for his own use

Beetroot On an errand o' mercy, lad. To rescue a fair maiden h'as is being 'eld prisoner—a once in a lifetime golden opportunity to get your name writ up in the book o' glory!

Soggy Cor!

Scabby I'd rather not 'ave my name in the book of glory, Sergeant—can't I stop at home?

Beetroot This is a 'ighly dangerous mission. I ain't *ordering* you to do it, Sonny-Jim—you're volunteering! "Ten-shun! Shoulder arms! Right—turn... As'y'were! Wait for it! Don't you know your right from your left, Scabby Tater-Blight? Right turn! By the right—quick march. Lef'-ri'-lef'-ri'-lef'-ri'-lef' ...

Scabby Tater-Blight and Soggy Boggart march off

(*Yelling after them*) 'Alt! (*He turns, smartly, and salutes the Crowman*) Permission to proceed with Operation Aunt Sally, sah?

Crowman Carry on, Sergeant. But you can tell Worzel Gummidge, from me, that I am giving him this one last chance. Just one more complaint against him and I shall convene the Scarecrow's Court.

Beetroot I'm sure that won't be necessary, sah.

Crowman Well, I hope so. Neglecting his duties—allowing the rooks to take over the Ten Acre Field—walking about in front of humans—conduct unbecoming a scarecrow, Sergeant.

Beetroot With respect, sah, you've got to make allowances for 'im being a bit soft in the head.

Crowman Sergeant, however stupid and humble a scarecrow may be, he carries in his turnip head the whole past and future of the scarecrow race. One false step—just one—and our entire empire of twigs and straw would crackle into oblivion—in the biggest bonfire this world has ever seen.

Beetroot Even Gummidge knows that, sah. But I think I know 'ow Gummidge must feel stuck out there on the brow of the 'ill in all weathers—no-one to call your friend—the dang-blasted cawing, caw, cawing of them rooks all day—it's a lonely life bein' a scarecrow.

Crowman It's a lonely life being the Crowman, Sergeant Beetroot. Where would all you scarecrows be if I took it into *my* head that life wasn't worth the candle and went into a decline?

Beetroot No. Don't do that, sah—there's a situation as don't bear thinking of . . .

Crowman Exactly.

Sergeant Beetroot salutes again, smartly, takes a place to the rear, turns about, and calls to his men off-stage

Beetroot Right, you 'orrible scarecrows! Let's see the kind of straw you're made of—by the right—quick march!

And Sergeant Beetroot marches off in the wake of his Scarecrows

The light has faded into dusk. The Crowman turns up the antique gas street-lamp. He crosses and continues the repair work he was carrying out on the Scarecrow at the beginning of Act II. The music of No. 15 creeps in behind

Crowman Scarecrows complaining of solitude! What is the world coming to? I wish I had a copper penny for every evening I've sat in this yard with nothing but a pen-knife and a bit of sandpaper for company . . . (*He sings*)

No. 15. Make Yourself A Friend

When you're feeling lonely,
And the road you're on
Is only
The beginning,
Not the end—
Make yourself a friend,
Make yourself a friend

When you're feeling older,
And the weather's getting colder
And there's nothing
Round the bend—
Make yourself a friend,
Make yourself a friend

All I've learned,
All I've discerned,

In this ragged old lifetime of mine,
Is a helping hand,
Someone to understand,
And with two of us—
Not just one of us—
The two of us would get along fine

When you need a brother,
And you never had no other
And for marriage it's too late,
Make yourself a mate—
A chum—
Someone—
A scarecrow in the sun,
Make yourself a friend,
My friend,
Make yourself a friend

The Lights fade to Black-out

SCENE 2

The Barn

There is complete darkness and then, suddenly, the barn is bathed in the glow of three lanterns, held by Sergeant Beetroot, Soggy Boggart and Scabby Tater-Blight. They hold up their lanterns to reveal Worzel sitting on a bale of hay with a bucket over his head

Beetroot Scarecrow Gummidge—show a leg there, lad—the drums and trumpets is a-summoning you to duty!
Soggy Wakey-wakey, Worzel! Rise and shine!
Beetroot Snap out of it, son—your Crowman an' your Country needs you! It's no good. An ordinary sulk is bad enough but his bucket sulk is awful.
Soggy Try sticking your pitchfork in him, Sarge.

Sergeant Beetroot raises his pitchfork, and then has second thoughts

Beetroot He wouldn't be no use to us if he was perforated. Come along now, Gummidge! Wakey, wakey!
Scabby Wake up, Worzel. We're going to rescue Aunt Sally!

Worzel comes round immediately at the mention of the name and pulls the bucket off his head

Worzel Who is?
Beetroot We four is. That's if you 'as the spirit for it!
Worzel You juss' lead me to where that bad-tempered ol' buzzard took 'er, Sergeant Beetroot, tha'ss all!
Beetroot Them's the sort of words I likes to 'ear! You go and scruffy

yourself up in a scarecrow-like manner—we'll muster outside the barn in five minutes' time.

Worzel I'll go and see if I can find my brave head. Then I'll kick the capoosal out of him. (*He exits*)

Sergeant Beetroot, Soggy Boggart and Scabby Tater-Blight move downstage and outside the barn where the night is bathed in moonlight

Beetroot Douse them lights, lads—Any scarecrow who ain't got the stomach for the job in 'and 'ad better say so now. I won't think any the less of him.

Soggy We're wiv you, Sarge!

Scabby Every inch of the way!

Beetroot Stout scarecrows! (*He sings*)

No. 16. We'll Be There

There's a carefree bunch of lads I know,
They're ready and they're rough,
They're the sort of chaps you want around
When the goin's getting tough.
They ain't all that to look at,
But they're brave and they are true,
The kind of pals a soldier needs
'Cos they're bound to see it through.
They're faithful and they're loyal,
And I'm proud to call 'em chums,
And to march along beside them
When we're summoned by the drums.
There's me an' 'im an' 'im as well
And they call us soldiers three
And would any of us turn and run?

Scabby   Only 'im an' 'im an' me . . .

Beetroot (*speaking*) Silence in the ranks! (*He sings*)
When the Bayonet glints and glitters
We'll be there

Scarecrows   We'll be there

Soggy   Even though we've got the jitters
We'll be there

Scarecrows   We'll be there

Beetroot   We are tough and we're tremendous
May our strong right arms defend us

Scabby   If you've got a right arm you c'n lend us
I'll be there

Scarecrows   We'll be there

Beetroot (*speaking*) That we will, lads. (*He sings*)
We are chaps as knows our duty
When we're there

Scarecrows   When we're there

Beetroot	Fight for England, 'ome and beauty When we're there
Scarecrows	When we're there
Beetroot	Our courage is enormous And our fame goes on before us
Scabby	Can I go back in the chorus?
Beetroot	You'll be there!
Scarecrows	He'll be there
Beetroot	When there's danger in the offing We'll be there
Scarecrows	We'll be there
Beetroot	We are lads who stop at nothing To get there
Scarecrows	To get there
Beetroot	Our strength it never wearies We don't even know what fear is
Soggy	But we know what drinking beer is— We'll be there
Scarecrows	We'll be there
Beetroot	When the cannons flash and thunder We'll be there
Scarecrows	We'll be there
Beetroot	Though the cowards pause and wonder We'll be there
Scarecrows	We'll be there
Beetroot	We are ready, we are willing We'll do anything that's thrilling
Soggy	We don't even stop at killing
Scabby (*speaking*)	Speak for yourself!
Scarecrows	We'll be there
Beetroot	In the thickest part of trouble We'll be there
Scarecrows	We'll be there
Beetroot	We come running at the double To get there
Scarecrows	To get there
Beetroot	Though our chances may be slender We shall write our names in splendour
Scabby	And I think I might surrender
Beetroot	You'll be there
Scabby **Soggy** }	We'll be there!

Worzel, carrying a pitchfork in the slope-arms position, enters and leads the Scarecrows in an eccentric march

No. 16A. Scarecrow's March

Worzel (*chanting*)
> We are the backbone on the Empire,
> Scarecrow breed are we,
> We are the boys who make no noise ...

There is an elaborate, stamping foot-changing routine as Worzel leads them off

> (*Speaking*) Come on, lads!

> *They exit*

SCENE 3

Outside Mr Shepherd's Cottage

The Lights fade up from dusk to dawn to reveal Aunt Sally, sitting in her attic window, wistfully singing

No. 17. Aunt Sally's song (Reprise)

Aunt Sally   Is there no more than this,
                  No Prince Charming's kiss
                  No glass-slipper ending ...?

At which point she breaks down and weeps copiously

> *Worzel, Sergeant Beetroot, Soggy Boggart and Scabby Tater-Blight enter, on tiptoe*

Worzel There she is! Tha'ss my Aunt Sally! 'Er didn't oughter wheep like that—she'll rust 'er pretty little 'inges!
Beetroot Right, rescue party forward to fight the foe—now!

Sergeant Beetroot prods Worzel to the front as Scabby and Soggy retreat to the rear and cower behind Sergeant Beetroot who is cowering behind Worzel

Worzel 'Ere—why for are you shovin' and a-pushin' ol' Worzel to the front?
Beetroot 'Ave no fear, Scarecrow Gummidge—me and the rest o' the lads is right behind you.
Scabby }
Soggy } (*together*) Oh arr, Worzel—that we is orlright—right behind you ...
Worzel Yes, that's what I'm afraid of. (*His knees knock together, but he summons his courage*) Don't you worry, Aunt Sal! I'll 'ave you rescood an' out o' there in two shakes o' a barmy badger's behind!

No. 17A. Rescue Music

The Rescue of Aunt Sally from Mr Shepherd's Cottage

1 *Sergeant Beetroot, Scabby and Worzel move towards the cottage and fall over.*

2 *They get up. Sergeant Beetroot calls for a ladder*

3 *Scabby and Soggy get the ladder, come back to the cottage and hang the ladder over the balcony*

4 *Sergeant Beetroot prods Worzel up the ladder and he falls through a missing rung half-way up. Business between Scabby and Soggy at the bottom of the ladder*

5 *Soggy runs* L, *Scabby runs* R. *They then run towards each other and Scabby does a back flip*

6 *Sergeant Beetroot takes the ladder and goes* L *of the cottage. Mr Shepherd appears through the front door. Sergeant Beetroot leans the ladder on the* L *side of the cottage*

7 *Mr Shepherd looks up at Worzel on the balcony. Worzel stands still and Scabby and Soggy run into the cottage*

8 **Mr Shepherd** What's Braithwaite's scarecrow doing on my balcony? *He goes into the cottage*

9 *There is the crash of crockery.*
   Mr Shepherd Get out of here! *Soggy appears through the flap, getting stuck*

10 **Mr Shepherd** And you! *Then Scabby comes through the front window*

11 *Soggy comes out of the cottage. Worzel gets the dummy Aunt Sally from upstairs and throws it to Scabby*

12 *Scabby throws it to Sergeant Beetroot. Mr Shepherd comes out of the front door. Soggy throws it to Mr Shepherd who takes it back indoors*

13 *Sergeant Beetroot shouts "Charge!" Soggy charges through the front door and right out the back where there is a loud crash of buckets*

14 *Scabby then tries to charge the door but it won't open. Meanwhile, Soggy goes back into the cottage through the back door*

15 *Sergeant Beetroot then tries the front door, opens it and goes in*

16 **Mr Shepherd** Let go of my Aunt Sally!
   Soggy I've got her, Worzel!
   Mr Shepherd Right, I've got you! *He then fires the blunderbus*

17 *Soggy tries the front window but there's nobody there so he gives dummy to Worzel upstairs*

18 *They both try to get the dummy through the attic window. There is the smashing of glass. The dummy won't go through. Meanwhile, Scabby is going up the ladder*

19 *Soggy goes down the stairs. Worzel tries to get the dummy through the* L *window and knocks Scabby off the ladder*

20 *Mr Shepherd comes out of the front door with the blunderbus. Scabby climbs back up the ladder on to the roof*

21 *Worzel comes downstairs and tries to get the dummy through the front window knocking Scabby off the ladder. Crash. Worzel gets back. Mr Shepherd sees him and aims the blunderbus at him. Worzel disappears as Mr Shepherd fires hitting Scabby who falls off the roof and into the water butt* L *of the cottage*

22 *Sergeant Beetroot and Soggy come out of the cottage waving a white flag and Mr Shepherd chases them off, shouting:* "Stand still while I get a decent shot at you!"

23 *Worzel and the real Aunt Sally come out of the house*

Aunt Sally (*throwing her arms wide ecstatically*) How romantic! Saved— saved by one whose heart is bigger than a lion's!

Worzel steps forward hopefully—but Sergeant Beetroot steps in front of him and Aunt Sally throws herself into Sergeant Beetroot's arms

My hero!

Worzel Oy! But Aunt Sally. It wor me wot done the rescuin'! Ol' Worzel— not that dang-blasted Beetroot! 'Tis yor Worzel as is your 'ero, Aunt Sal—the one wot loves you most in all the world.

Aunt Sally (*to Beetroot*) Would you excuse me please? (*To Worzel*) You! 'Ow could you be anybody's hero? You pong. Why—you ain't even good enough to clean my boots.

With which she saunters off on the arm of Sergeant Beetroot

Worzel (*calling after them*) Yes, I is! I can clean yor boots as good as 'ee can, missis! You juss bring 'em 'ere an' I'll clean 'em for you better'n you ever 'ad 'em cleaned before! Aunt Sally—do you 'ear me! (*He looks around frustrated, and spots a pile of potatoes*) You come back 'ere—afore I 'its you on the back of the 'ead with one of these potaties!

And he slings a potato after Aunt Sally, followed by another—and another. We hear the crash of breaking glass. Worzel freezes as he hears the Crowman

Crowman (*off*) Worzel Gummidge!

The Crowman storms on holding up his hat which has a potato embedded in it

Is this your doing?

Worzel M-m-m-me, your eminence? Why for would ol' Worzel chuck a tatie at your highness?

Crowman Worzel Gummidge! I am the Crowman! Don't try and lie to me!

Worzel No, your flatulence. It *was* me, beggin' your pardon, sir—but it wor an accident.

Crowman Then it was one accident too many—follow me!

Worzel If it's all the same to you I'd rather not.
Crowman I said, follow me!

SCENE 4

The Barn Wall and Bench

There is a high barn wall with a bench in front of it

PC Parsons, sucking his pencil, accompanies an agitated Mr Shepherd

PC Parsons How many of them do you say there were, Mr Shepherd?
Mr Shepherd Half a dozen at the very least. I'd say they were a gang of international thieves.
PC Parsons International kidnappers more like. Didn't you say they'd kidnapped your Auntie Annie?
Mr Shepherd Aunt Sally, Constable Parsons! Aunt Sally!
PC Parsons (*crossing out what he has already written*) 'Ang about—let's get the facts down proper. (*Writing again*) International kidnappers kidnapped your Aunt Sally. What for, do you reckon, Mr Shepherd? Has the poor old dear got a few quid tucked away—or are they after her old age pension?
Mr Shepherd She ain't my *real* Aunt Sally! She's my wooden antique figure what was at the fête last Saturday—leastways, she would have been if somebody hadn't have pinched her—probably the same ugly-looking rascal and his accomplices who have got her now.
PC Parsons (*again crossing out what he has written*) 'Ang about—let's begin again. We'll want a proper description first.

Mrs Bloomsbury-Barton, who is passing, pauses to join in the conversation. She carries her handbag and umbrella

Mrs Bloomsbury-Barton I think I can assist you there, Constable Parsons. About six foot tall with wild tangled hair and a long horrible nose.

PC Parsons writes furiously

PC Parsons I'm much obliged to you, Mrs Bloomsbury-Barton ... "wild tangled nose and a long horrible hair". (*To Mr Shepherd*) She's a bit of a funny-looking old bird then, your Auntie Nancy?
Mr Shepherd 'Ow many more times? She ain't my Auntie Annie and she ain't my Aunt Nancy! She's my Aunt Sally, PC Parsons!
Mrs Bloomsbury-Barton And the description I have given you is a description of the rapscallion that's been terrorizing the village! Good heavens, Constable, you *pursued* him, man! A gaunt evil-looking rapscallion. Almost, in a manner of speaking, with a scarecrow look about him.

As the scene progresses, Scarecrows are tiptoeing on behind Mrs Bloomsbury-Barton, PC Parsons and Mr Shepherd. They gesticulate and prance about silently, mocking the conversation about Rookroster Day

PC Parsons (*writing in his notebook*) "... evil-looking with a scarecrow look about ..." (*He again crosses out what he has written*) I can't go writing that down in my notebook, can I? Under distinguishing marks or features—looks like a scarecrow! My super would go potty ... Oh, you mean *him*! Yes. Why didn't you say so? International criminal? A scarecrow? He don't look like neither of them. He looks like what he is— he looks like a tramp. And you ought to know better too, Mrs Bloomsbury-Barton, than to go mentioning scarecrows today of all days.

Mrs Bloomsbury-Barton What's today got to do with it?

PC Parsons Consult your calendar, ma'am. It's Rookroster Day.

Mr Shepherd So it is, an' all! I'd forgotten!

Mrs Bloomsbury-Barton Pah! Ignorant superstition!

Mr Shepherd It don't do to scoff at local folklore, ma'am.

PC Parsons That it don't—it's a widely held belief round these parts that scarecrows comes alive and walks and talks on Rookroster Day.

Mrs Bloomsbury-Barton Local mumbo-jumbo, Constable.

PC Parsons All 'orrible they say they are, these scarecrows, and all 'eadless they are!

No. 17B. Rookroster Day (Instrumental)

Mr Shepherd They're heralded, one story goes, by an awful hoot of an owl.

There is an owl hoot

But I don't pay no 'eed to it myself.

Mrs Bloomsbury-Barton I should hope not!

Unnoticed by PC Parsons, one of the Scarecrows has purloined his helmet while another has taken Mr Shepherd's hat. The Scarecrows swiftly transpose the headgear to the wrong heads

PC Parsons They go riding around, some of 'em, on an 'aunted haycart, or so they reckons. Not that I believes in them personally ...

The headgear is once again on the move. Mr Shepherd's hat finishes up back on his head. PC Parsons' helmet is passed from twiggy hand and finishes up hanging from a hayfork

Suddenly realizing that he is helmetless, PC Parsons looks around, sees his helmet, rushes to retrieve it and runs off. Mr Shepherd, oblivious of the adventures his hat has been having, also moves off

Mrs Bloomsbury-Barton sits, her handbag on one side, her umbrella on the other. The Scarecrows deftly switch them round

Mrs Bloomsbury-Barton I should think not too. Hogwash and piffle, walking and talking scarecrows ... (*She registers that her handbag and umbrella have been changed round and his puzzled*) Thank goodness there are a few of us in this village who can stand our guard ...

Once more the handbag and umbrella are switched

Don't you agree, PC Parsons and Mr Shepherd?

She looks round and is confronted by two Scarecrows

With a shriek, Mrs Bloomsbury-Barton takes to her heels

SCENE 5

Inside the Crowman's House

Which is as eccentric inside as it was out: a rickety building with lots of nooks and crannies, many of which appear to have been tacked on to the main structure as afterthoughts

John and Sue are concealed in the loft, and will not appear until later. The entire company of Scarecrows is assembled under the beady eye of Sergeant Beetroot who is trying to form them into some semblance of line. He carries a pitchfork

Beetroot Take your dressing by the right, you cackhanded clodhoppers! Let's have you standing in a smart and scarecrow-like manner! C'mon, c'mon! Chins in, chests h'out! This is a court of law—not a blackberry-picking outing! Smartly does it now—here comes his worship! For our creator, his honour the Crowman.

At which point, the Crowman enters, carrying an armful of official documentation

Company of Scarecrows—attenshun! ... Stan'-at-ease! ... Atten-*shun*! ... Stan'-at-ease! ... Atten-*shun*! Stan'-at-ease! Atten——
Crowman Very well, Sergeant Beetroot—that's more than sufficient.
Beetroot Sah!
Crowman Are we all assembled?
Beetroot Scarecrow Company all present and correct. Sah!

The Crowman looks around approvingly at his assembled Scarecrows

Crowman Our Testament ... for winter we're provided ... (*He sings*)

No. 18. Scarecrow's Hymn (Version II)

Barley for cheer,
All this is reason,
Sow seed and reap,
Season follow season.
Nature shall take her course,
Earth must lie fallow,
Rivers run deep,
Summertime run shallow.

Scarecrows   Holly for everlasting,
                        Mistletoe for mystery,
                        Only the scarecrows know
                        That the future is history.

A moment of reverent silence

Crowman This court is in session! Bring in the prisoner!
Beetroot Sah!

Sergeant Beetroot raises his pitchfork to the slope and marches out. He returns a moment later, escorting Worzel who has been trussed up with a rope which restricts his arms and legs so that as Sergeant Beetroot prods him forward with his pitchfork, Worzel is obliged to hop rather than walk. Worzel is blubbering copiously

Worzel Mercy, Mr Crowman, sir, your worship, your honour, your high and mightiness-ship. Whatever it is I done, yer 'oliness, I didn't mean to do it, an' I won't never do it no more, I swears it. Not nohow, not never. Just gi' me one more charnst, your all-forgiveness ...
Crowman Untie the prisoner and put him in the dock.
Worzel Don't put me in no dock, Mr Crowman, sir—it'll bring me out all over in turnip-blight, so it will ...
Crowman Worzel Gummidge, hold thy tongue while thou has a tongue in thy head to hold!
Beetroot Right then! Three volunteers—you, you and you—untie the prisoner and put him in the dock!

The three Scarecrows nominated untie Worzel and place him in the improvized dock

Crowman Sergeant Beetroot, swear in the jury.
Beetroot Sah! All of you, touch your heads and repeat after me—"May this head end up in the pig-swill bucket if I do not well and truly try Worzel Gummidge and find him guilty. Amen."
Worzel T'ain't fair!
Crowman Silence.

The Scarecrows touch their heads in grotesque attitudes as they mumble and bob up and down while repeating the oath in snatches

Read the charge, Sergeant Beetroot.
Beetroot Very good, sah! ... With respect, sah—can't read. Sah!
Crowman Very well, I shall read it myself. Worzel Hedgerow Gummidge——
Worzel Yes?
Crowman Be quiet! You are charged with that on divers occasions you were a nuisance and thorn in the side, that you roamed the countryside making trouble instead of carrying out your duties, that you abused the gift of speech and movement bestowed upon you, that you used your thinking head as a football and that you knocked off my hat with a potato. How do you plead?
Worzel I dunno, your majesty, I never pled.

Crowman Not guilty, I suppose. You always were a terrible liar. Who is the prosecutor?

Worzel Wassat, then? What's a prossy—possy—pussy—What 'is 'igh an' mightiness said?

Beetroot Prosecutor, lad. The one that points the finger of scorn at you and tells his worship what a bad lad you've been. Summon the prosecutor!

No. 18A. Music

Aunt Sally enters and gives her peculiar curtsy to the Crowman

Worzel Aunt Sally—what you doin' 'ere?

Beetroot Aunt Sally is the prosecutor, lad.

Worzel Aunt Sally? T'aint fair! Whyfor should Aunt Sally prossy—possy—pussy—call me a bad lad fer? She's worse nor what I am.

Aunt Sally Ho no I h'arn't.

Worzel Oh yes you is!

Aunt Sally Oh no I h'arn't! (*etc.*)

Beetroot You 'eard what Aunt Sally said, laddy. She h'arn't!

Worzel Oh—an' what's it got to do with you, you ugly ol' beetroot face?

Beetroot *Sergeant* Ugly Old Beetroot Face to you, Sonny Jim! I'll tell you what it's got to do with me. Aunt Sally and I have a little understanding.

Worzel You never!

Beetroot Ho yes, we 'ave! You've been so busy chucking potatoes about you don't know what's been going on under your long nose, you 'orrible little scarecrow! . . . (*Catching the Crowman's eye*) Beg pardon, sah—got carried away, sah!

Worzel (*miserably*) Tell me it ain't true, Aunt Sally. Tell me you ain't a-goin' to marry this ol' swollen beetroot, what's on'y good fer slicin' an' picklin'?

Aunt Sally I don't know, do I? Not at this immediate moment. I may marry him—on the other hand, I may not. We shall have to see.

Crowman (*banging his gavel*) If Aunt Sally doesn't get on with this case for the prosecution, Aunt Sally is going to find herself back in a trunk in Mr Shepherd's attic!

Aunt Sally (*bobbing demurely*) Yes, sir. Sorry, sir. At once, sir.

Crowman Let the trial commence. And Worzel . . .

Worzel Yes, sir.

Crowman Be very careful what you say. If you're found guilty you know what the sentence will be then, don't you?

Worzel No, sir.

Crowman Oh yes, you do. You know what happened to Tatty Bogle when he went to sleep in Farmer Thompson's best bed and wouldn't get up?

Worzel He was dug into the—dug into—dug into the . . .

Crowman Go on, Worzel.

Worzel Please, your almightiness. The words won't come out of my lips.

Crowman Tatie Bogle was dug into the compost heap! Continue, Aunt Sally.

Aunt Sally (*bobbing obsequiously*) Yes, your honour. Worzel 'Edgerow
Gummidge. Is it or is it not a fact that you wilfully and deliberately
threw—(*she produces exhibit "A" with a flourish*)—this King Edward
potato at—(*lowering her voice in awe*)—his honour the Crowman?

Cries of "Oh" and gasps of horror from the jury

Worzel Your eminence, I swears on my robin redbreast's life, I never on
purpose threwed no potatie at your 'igh and mightiness. I wouldn't, sir! I
might be stewpid but I ain't barmy.

Aunt Sally Worzel 'Edgerow Gummidge. Do you deny that this is a potato?

She passes him the potato and he takes a huge bite out of it

Worzel It's a potatie all right.

Aunt Sally If it was not throwed by you, how did it come into contact with
his honour's hat?

Worzel Pardon?

Aunt Sally Answer the question.

Worzel You're getting me all muddled and maddled, modom. The potato
was throwed by me, but I worn't throwing it at his majesty the Crowman.
I was on'y trying to do my job, your worship, sir. I was throwin' them
there potaties at the dang-blasted rooks.

Crowman Worzel, you went to Scarecrow School, did you not?

Worzel Oh, I did that, sir. That's where I learnt to talk yakity like what you
read in books out of from to.

Crowman And were you taught that the way to scare crows is to bombard
them with potatoes?

Laughter in court

Worzel I was not, sir. But beggin' yer crowmanship's parding, I was desprit,
yer honour, sir. See, him what runs Scatterbrook, he's thinking o' buying
a 'lectric crow-scarer——

Gasps of consternation from the jury

Crowman I know all about that, Worzel. And the main reason why you're
here is that your behaviour is bringing that day nearer. If all these
scarecrows are replaced by electronic crow-scarers, it will be because
Worzel Gummidge has given hard-working scarecrows a bad name.

*Worzel hangs his head in mortification. Cries of "Shame!", "Chuck him on the
bonfire!", "Feed him to the pigs!", "Pull him to pieces!" etc. The Crowman
bangs his gavel for order. Sergeant Beetroot holds the angry jury at bay with
his pitchfork*

Beetroot Jury subdued, sah!

Crowman Aunt Sally, do you intend to question any witnesses?

Aunt Sally If your honour pleases, call Aunt Sally.

Beetroot Call Aunt Sally ...

Crowman What?

Worzel She's even more stewpid nor what I am. How can you axe yourself questions, you wooden-'eaded clothes-prop?

Aunt Sally You'll see. (*She crosses to the witness-box*) I swear on this wheatsheaf that I will tell the truth, some of the truth and most of the truth, so long as it suits me. (*Then, commencing her own cross-examination*) Is my name Aunt Sally? Yes, it is. Can I prove I am who I say I am? Course I can! How? 'Cos nobody else has got such elligant elbows and delicate hands. Will I tell the court about last Friday? Yes, I will. Last Friday I was walking along the High Street when who should stop me but a hulking great stewpid scarecrow. Is that hulking great stewpid scarecrow in court? Yes, he is. Can I point him out? Yes, I can——

The Crowman bangs his gavel

Crowman (*more wearily than before*) Aunt Sally, is it your intention that we should have to endure much more of this?

Aunt Sally Oh, yes, your honour. *Lots* more. Why—I've only just started!

Crowman Then it's *my* intention to shut you up. (*He bangs his gavel again*) I shall adjourn this court in order that Aunt Sally may prepare her closing speech for the prosecution—with due regard to brevity. Sergeant Beetroot—stand the court down.

Beetroot Sah! Members of the court—be upstanding for his honour the Crowman!

The entire court shambles to its feet the Crowman sweeps out

Scarecrow jury—at rest!

No. 18B. Eerie Music

Upon which order, the entire assembly, with the exception of Sergeant Beetroot, stiffen into grotesque rigid scarecrow postures. Sergeant Beetroot paces up and down, holding his pitchfork like a swagger stick. He taps a Scarecrow's drooping arms; he resumes his pacing. Then, as the Lights fade into eerie shadows, Sergeant Beetroot pauses, yawns, and droops. He too is rigid. John and Sue appear from out of their hiding place in the loft. They clamber down the steps and peer at the Scarecrows, a trifle fearfully

Sue I'm frightened, John—are you sure it's safe?

John Course it's safe—they've all gone to sleep.

Sue Let's get out while we've got the chance.

John And leave Worzel?

Sue But supposing they find us? What will they do?

John What can they do? They're only scarecrows.

Sergeant Beetroot suddenly yawns

Sue Look out!

The children dart for fresh cover as Aunt Sally also shows signs of life

Aunt Sally Sergeant? How long 'as the Crowman been gone?

Beetroot leans his pitchfork against the dock where Worzel stands motionless in the scarecrow position. Immediately, one of Worzel's eyes opens and his head turns in the direction of the pitchfork. Beetroot plunges into his shapeless greatcoat and produces his battered alarm clock. He shakes it, then stares at it for a while

Beetroot He's been gone a long time. That means he should be back in—let me see—a short time.
Aunt Sally Thank you.

Beetroot's eye falls on Worzel

Beetroot And I wouldn't like to be in *your* boots when he does get back.

Worzel's head is the only part of him that moves

Worzel An' I wouldn't like to be in your boots any time—you stinking old beetroot. Whoever 'eard of a beetroot bein' a scarecrow?
Beetroot It's all the rage at this moment of time. Ain't it, Aunt Sally?
Aunt Sally I don't know, I'm sure. I don't mix socially with scarecrows. They're far too inferior.

Murmurs of dissent from the Scarecrow jury

Worzel Heh heh! That's tellin' 'im, Aunt Sally.
Beetroot That wasn't what you told me in Mr Shepherd's potting shed, my dear. You said I was your 'ero.
Aunt Sally Only because you got me out of the stupid old trunk. You don't think I meant it, do you? All you scarecrows are the same—stupid, ignorant, common and dirty!

The murmurs of dissent grow louder and more menacing. The jury of Scarecrows are making threatening gestures at Aunt Sally. Sergeant Beetroot turns on the Scarecrow jury as the hubbub rises even louder, and they rise threateningly

Beetroot You horrible row of turnips! Anyone who tangles with this lady tangles with me!

It is the moment Worzel has been waiting for. While Sergeant Beetroot's attention is turned on the jury, he snatches up the pitchfork

Worzel An' anyone as tangles with Worzel tangles with this. Ooo arr! (*Prodding Beetroot with it*) Keep back, Sergeant Beetroot, unless you want turnin' into piccalilli! Come on, Aunt Sally, we're leaving!
Beetroot Best go with him, my dear. I can't control this rabble without that there pitchfork.
Aunt Sally Where are we going, Worzel?

During the following, Worzel, with Aunt Sally at his side, is backing towards the door brandishing the pitchfork with a good deal of menace, while the Scarecrows cautiously advance on them

Worzel Anywhere! Egypt! Bulgaria! Americky! Any o' those places you's allus talkin' of—I'm not stayin' 'ere to be dug into no compost 'eap! (*To the Scarecrows*) Not so brave now, is you—now that Worzel's got 'is dander up?

The Crowman enters and stands behind Worzel

The Scarecrows abruptly shuffle to a stop as they see the Crowman. Worzel, however, is unaware of his presence, and believes the Scarecrow's hesitancy is due to their fear of himself

Jus' look at 'em, Aunt Sally. Lot o' cowardy custards. (*Jeering*) Cowardy—cowardy custard, cowardy—cowardy cus—— (*He backs into the Crowman*) Ooooh arr. (*He realizes, to his horror, what he has done*) AAAAR! (*Dropping the pitchfork and falling to his knees*) M—m—m—muh—muh . . . 'Ello, your 'ighness, I was jus' goin' for a little walkie.
Crowman (*cutting short Worzel's blabberings*) Back! All of you! (*And he strikes a match; angrily*) Or there'll be a big *bonfire* tonight.
Beetroot Do as the Crowman says! Jump to it now—look lively!

The Scarecrows scutter back to their places—Worzel making the quickest progress despite the fact that he is still on his knees

Aunt Sally Shall I continue with my evidence, your honour?
Crowman After that disgraceful exhibition, Aunt Sally, I think further evidence is unnecessary. Scarecrows of the jury—do you find the prisoner guilty or not guilty?

No. 19. Guilty

Jury	He is guilty, he is guilty,
	He is definitely guilty,
	He is naughty, he is nasty,
	He is cheap!
	He's unlawful,
	He is awful,
	There is evidence by the drawerful,
	We demand you throw him on the
	Compost heap!
Worzel	I'll be good, I'll be good,
	I'll be so dang good,
	I'll be gooder'n the goodest kid in Sunday school,
	I'll do ev'rythin' that's right,
	I'll be nice an' perlite,
	I'll only speak when I'm spoken to—I'll make it a rule
	I'll be good, I'll be good,
	I'll be so pesky good,
	I won't kick Aunt Sally, I'll do everythin' to please 'er
	I'll say thank you, I'll say please,
	I'll go down on my knees,
	I'll even use a hankychief to blow my 'ooter.

Worzel wipes his nose on his sleeve

Aunt Sally (*speaking*) Disgusting.
  (*Singing*)   You are guilty, you are guilty,
                 You are absolutely guilty,
                 You are wicked, you are wanton,
                 You're a liar!
                 You are rotten,
                 Misbegotten,
                 You're so many things I've forgotten,
                 But enough to have you tossed on
                 The Bonfire!
Worzel   I'll be nice, I'll be nice,
                 I'll be ever so nice,
                 I'll be the nicest scarecrow that there's ever been,
                 I'll do my duty in Ten Acre,
                 I'll pay homage to my maker,
                 I'll keep all my straw an' my twiggy ends clean.
                 I'll be nice, I'll be nice,
                 I'll be so pesky nice,
                 Even tho' a scarecrow's life is awf'lly lonely,
                 I'll be positively charmin',
                 I'll be utterly disarmin',
                 But I begs you, your eminence, DON'T DISOWN ME . . .

Crowman (*speaking*) Worzel, the jury has decided. (*To the jury*) And having found him guilty do you find the prisoner guilty or very guilty?

Jury (*singing*)
                 He is guilty, he is guilty,
                 He is definitely guilty,
                 He is evil, he's a weevil,
Crowman   I'm annoyed
                 That this scarecrow I created
                 Had the gall to raise my hatred
                 I pronounce that Worzel Gummidge
                 Be destroyed!

The Crowman's final lines have been delivered with such vehemence that Worzel falls to his knees, a quivering wreck.

Worzel No, no—your benificence—not destroyed—not ol' Worzel . . .
Crowman Rise and face your maker!

Worzel shambles to his feet. The Crowman formally dons his hat

Worzel Hedgerow Gummidge, you have been found very guilty. It is, therefore, the verdict of this Scarecrow Court that you shall be removed from this place and taken to a compost heap, where you will remain for a period not exceeding one crop rotation, after which time you will be dug into——

John and Sue burst out from their hiding place

John No! Stop!

At the first sound of human voices all of the Scarecrows, with the exception of Worzel, freeze themselves into the scarecrow position

Crowman Bless my soul! What are you children doing here? What have you seen?

Sue Everything! And if you dig Worzel into the compost heap, we're going to tell the police you're holding him prisoner!

Although the Scarecrows are frozen, their eyes twitch menacingly

Crowman My dear child, these are scarecrows! How can it be a crime to kidnap a few bundles of straw and a wooden doll!

Worzel You'll 'ave to excuse 'em, your magnificence. They don't know no better. (*To the children*) What are you trying to do—get me into trouble?

John I like that! We're trying to get you *out* of trouble.

Crowman It's too late for that, young man. Worzel has already had a fair trial.

John Call that a fair trial? I've seen trials on television. You haven't heard the defence.

Crowman What could anyone possibly say in defence of Worzel Gummidge? You'd better leave. Your father must be wondering where you are.

Sue And Mr Shepherd must be wondering where his Aunt Sally is too. And if we tell him you've stolen her, you'll never be allowed to make a scarecrow again, and then you'll starve.

Crowman A spirited young lady, aren't you? Very well. Do I understand you wish to make a speech for the defence?

John YES!

Crowman Then you may do so.

Worzel beams. The beam slowly fades from his face and he shuffles, uneasily, as he gradually realizes that John can't think of anything to say in his defence.

What have you to say in Worzel's favour?

Sue He ... well ... er ... no.

John He sort of ... well, once ... no.

Worzel Thank you very much indeed! (*Coming to his own rescue*) There was one time when I ... and then I ... and another time when I ... but I ... no, I didn't.

John Er ... Can we have time to think?

Crowman I'm afraid that time is already up. Worzel Hedgerow Gummidge——

Sue Wait! Wait! I know! He's kind to his robin redbreast.

Crowman What robin redbreast?

Worzel The one that lives in my stumick, your grace an' favour. (*He feels inside his jacket and produces his robin*)

No. 19A. Romantic Worzel (Instrumental)

Crowman But I got rid of that robin's nest years ago—when I cleared all the fieldmice out of your elbows.

Worzel So you did, your gloryship. But she'd nowhere to go, sir. So bein' kind in the 'ead, I let 'er come back inside. (*He returns the robin to the safety of his "stumick"*)

Sue And he feeds her on biscuit crumbs and blackberries and every Sunday he gives her a whole bottle of milk.

Aunt Sally *Steals* her a whole bottle of milk, more like.

Worzel Finds it, Aunt Sally—finds it. They leaves it lying about on doorsteps—every morning o' the week.

Sue So if you throw Worzel on the compost heap, what will his robin redbreast do?

Aunt Sally Fly away, of course, you silly little girl!

Worzel Ah, but 'er can't fly away, see!

Crowman Why not?

Worzel 'Er's nestin'. 'Er's got four little tweeties—come and 'ave a look.

A Scarecrow Sweeties, Worzel?

Worzel Not sweeties—tweeties! Don't make any noise or you might wake 'em up.

The Scarecrows and John and Sue crowd round and peer at his "stumick"

Come and have a look, your high and mightiness!

The Crowman also takes a look. He rubs his hands in delight at having an excuse to let Worzel off

Crowman Four young 'uns. Very well, Worzel, you've saved your neck this time. Sergeant?

Beetroot Sah!

Crowman Clear the court. Case dismissed.

Aunt Sally Disgraceful—I shall appeal.

She stamps out. Beetroot ushers the Scarecrow jury out

Worzel, likewise, tries to leave. During the following, the Crowman's house is struck

Crowman Not you, Worzel! I haven't quite finished as far as you're concerned. You may have lived to fight another day, but remember, Worzel Gummidge, my patience isn't entirely inexhaustible.

Worzel No, your eminence.

Crowman And if Mr Braithwaite of Scatterbrook decides to throw you in the dustbin because you're idle, incorrigible and incompetent—don't look to me for any help. And those are my final words.

Worzel Thank 'ee very much, sir. (*He touches his hat ingratiatingly*)

The Crowman glowers at Worzel, then turns on his heel and walks away

Only Worzel and John and Sue are left on-stage. During the following, the scenery moves in behind them, forming:

Scene 6

The Barn

Worzel is still touching his hat at the retreating figure of the Crowman

Worzel (*rounding on John and Sue*) What do you two think you're staring at? Go on them—shove off out of it.

John I like that! After we helped to save your life.

Sue You might at least say "thank you", Worzel.

Worzel What 'ave I got to thank anybody for? All my scarecrow friends 'ave pushed off.

John I thought *we* were your friends.

Worzel You's just titchy yewmans—I'm talkin' about proper scarecrow friends to share my special day with.

Sue What's so special about today?

John It's his birthday.

Worzel How do you know?

John It's always your birthday.

Worzel It isn't always me birthday. Anyways, this one's different—'cos this is my bestest birthday. That's the one that scarecrows 'ave for their 'ead— 'cos when you gets your 'ead, that's when you comes alive, see? 'Ere— would you like me to tell you about my bestest birthday?

John Not a lot.

Worzel I thought you would . . . (*He sings*)

No. 20 It's Me Birthday

I wor builded by the Crowman out of straw an' string.
Down in Ten Acre Field of a Saturday morn,
For to keep them ol' crows up there on the wing,
Instead o' down 'ere a-peckin' at the corn.
Through winter an' summer an' autumn an' spring,
For many a year all tattered and torn—
But suddenly I've remembered a very funny thing
Today's the anniversary of when I was born—
It's me birthday

John He says it once a week!
Worzel It's me birthday
Sue He's got ever such a cheek!
Worzel It's me birthday
John If he even dares to speak!
Worzel It's me birthday!
It's me birthday!
It's the day that I got made,
It's me birthday,
There should be a grand parade,
It's me birthday,
Get it publicly displayed,

	'Cos it's me birthday!
	It's me birthday
John	He has told us all before!
Worzel	It's me birthday
Sue	If he says it just once more!
Worzel	It's me birthday
John	I will knock him through the floor!
Worzel	It's me birthday
John	It's his birthday,
Sue	It's the day he likes the best,
	It's his birthday,
	He can have his trousers pressed,
	It's his birthday,
	He can be a proper pest,
	'Cos it's his birthday,
Worzel	It's me birthday,
	It's the day I like the most
John ⎫	
Sue ⎭	It's his birthday
Worzel	I can't wait to get the post!
John ⎫	
Sue ⎭	It's his birthday
Worzel	All stand up and drink a toast!
All	'Cos it's his birthday
	It's his birthday
Worzel	It's me birthday!

(*Speaking*) Right, seeing as it's me bestest birthday and you're my bestest friends, where's me present then . . .?

John and Sue run off

(*Calling after them*) You can fetch me my Aunt Sally all wrapped up in tinsel and sillyphane!

No. 20A. Mysterioso

Worzel crosses into:

SCENE 7

A lonely field

The Crowman is putting the finishing touches to a new Scarecrow

Crowman Good-day to you, Worzel.

Worzel Good-day to you, Mr Crowman, your effervescence, sir. Tha'ss a fine scarecrow you've got there—'ee'll do a grand job scarin' rooks.

Crowman A grander job I don't doubt, Worzel, than a certain scarecrow that shall be nameless who should be on duty in Ten Acre Field.

Worzel I wor juss' on my way there, Mr Crowman, sir—goin' hot lickertisl-pit I wor an' all—when I 'appened to catch a glimpse of your 'ighness, an' it seemed on'y right an' proper to stop an' pass the time o' day. What's 'is name?

Crowman It will be Hessian Tatersack and today's his birthday, Worzel.

Worzel Oh no, yer inexactitude—that can't be right. Today's *my* birthday, d'y'see?

Crowman Worzel Gummidge, today can be your birthday—it can also be Hessian Tatersack's birthday.

Worzel 'Ow's that then? Tha'ss too much for a turnip 'eaded scarecrow to take in all at once.

Crowman Where's your thinking head, Worzel?

Worzel Back in Scatterbrook farmyard, sir, with a weighty problem on its mind—Percy the Pig is sitting on it.

Crowman Well—perhaps you can learn to comprehend it a different way—stand over there and watch.

No. 20B. Scarecrow's Hymn (Instrumental Reprise)

(*He takes a twig from his pocket; breaking it over the Scarecrow's head and performing the same incantations as before*)

Apples for health,
Corn for plenty,
Berries for happiness,
By the wind and the rain and all the seasons . . .
I name this scarecrow Hessian Tatersack.

(*He removes his hat and becomes more solemn*) Hessian Tatersack, I am the Crowman. As the rain is to the crops, and wind to the seeds, as the sun is to berries, so is the Crowman to all things of twigs and straw. And I give thee life . . .

The new Scarecrow twitches into life

Worzel Dang me, Mr Crowman—you've done it again! You've breathed him!

Crowman Exactly as I did to you, Worzel, all that time ago.

The Crowman and Hessian exchange bows

Face me—arms down—follow me. Now, Worzel, wish him a happy being born day.

Worzel But it ain't fair, you illuminescence! 'Tis my birthday 'ee's pinched!

Crowman Worzel Gummidge! You have had more birthdays than any creature under the sun. And still you refuse to learn—the magic of birthdays only works when they are shared. Share yours with Hessian Tatersack.

Worzel Do I 'ave to, your majestickness?

The Crowman nods. Worzel reluctantly sets about the task

Crowman Go on, then!

Worzel I's a-goin' on! I's just gettin' a run up to 'im! (*Approaching Hessian*) A very 'appy bein' born day, Hessian Tatersack.

Hessian (*struggling with the words*) A very 'appy—bestest—birthday to 'ee, Worzel Gummidge.

No. 20C. Worzel's Birthday

Worzel My my my! Did you 'ear that, Mr Crowman? Them's the fust words 'e ever spoke an' 'e spake 'em to ol' Worzel! 'E's coming properly to life now, ain't 'e, Mr Crowman? An' me bein' nice to 'im 'elped.

Crowman Giving is best.

Worzel Did you 'ear what the Crowman said, Hessian—giving is best.

Hessian (*indistinctly*) Gevin'—is—bess.

Worzel Not gevin'—is—bess! Giving is best! A very happy bestest being born day to 'ee, Hessian!

Hessian And a very happy bestest birthday to you, Worzel.

The stage is suddenly full of Scarecrows, including Sergeant Beetroot, bringing birthday presents. They do an elaborate hat-raising, leg-shaking scarecrow bow as they greet Worzel

Scarecrows A very happy bestest birthday, Worzel . . . Very happy being-born day, Hessian Tatersack.

Worzel My my my, I never knowned I knowed so many friends. Thass Scarecrow Bowing an' Scrapin', thass what that is, Hessian. Now you an' me 'as to do some bowin' an' scrapin' back—you watch ol' Worzel an' learn from 'im.

He teaches Hessian the bowing and scraping routine

Thass it! Me an' you's sharin' this birthday a fair ol' treat!

Aunt Sally minces in, all sweetness and light

Aunt Sally What about sharing your birthday cake then, Worzel?

Worzel What birthday cake?

Aunt Sally Well, is there cake or isn't there? I ain't stopping if there ain't cake!

Worzel I'll have to ask Mr Crowman but he's busy . . . Please, your omnipotence. For Aunt Sally's sake can there be cake? Just this once.

Crowman Very well, Worzel—cake there shall be—just this once.

Aunt Sally Well—perhaps I might stop just this once.

The Crowman claps his hands. A large cake appears from the flies—but not large enough for Aunt Sally who is about to flounce off

Crowman Aunt Sally—that's only a replica!

No. 20D. Birthday Cake Music

He claps his hands again and an enormous birthday cake descends. Sighs of delight from Aunt Sally and the Scarecrows

John and Sue enter with presents

John ⎫
Sue ⎬ (*together*) Happy birthday, Worzel!

Worzel What are you three titchy yewmans doing 'ere? I 'ope you ain't just turned up for a slice o' my cake?

John I like that!

Sue Blinkin' cheek!

Worzel Now you're 'ere I suppose you can stop—there's enough of it to give you both a titchy slice.

Crowman Take your partners for the Scarecrow Hop!

Worzel advances to dance with Aunt Sally but Hessian is ahead of him

Worzel 'Ere y'are, Aunt Sally, cop 'old ... (*To Hessian*) You let go o' that there arm, Hessian Tatersack, else I'll screw your 'ead off an' boil it in a pot for me tea!

Crowman Sharing, Worzel, sharing!

Worzel Anything but my Aunt Sally!

Crowman You don't own much, I'll grant you—it's a scarecrow fact of life. Isn't that so, Sergeant Beetroot?

Beetroot Defferably, sah! H'us scarecrows h'is h'impecunious to a fault—sah!

No. 21. Slice Of Cake (Reprise)

Beetroot	We don't live very expensive,
Scabby	We ain't got silks nor riches,
Soggy	Our wardrobe's 'ardly extensive,
	A couple o' rags an' some stitches,
	We don't 'ave much, just scraps an' such,
	All worldly goods we're lackin',
Beetroot	A Scarecrow's bed where 'e lays 'is 'ead
	Is a 'eap 'o straw an' some sackin'.
Hessian	On t'other 'and 'e don't need a lot
	To stop 'im gettin' tearful—
Beetroot	Just three things—one cold, one 'ot
All	An' both of 'em keeps 'im cheerful

Led by the Crowman playing a flute, the Scarecrows go into a joyous dance, with Worzel partnering Aunt Sally, Sergeant Beetroot partnering Sue and another Scarecrow partnering John

All	A slice o' cake an' a cup of tea,
	Suits Aunt Sally an' that suits me,
	Offer us the world but all we'll take
	Is a cup o' tea an' a slice of cake.
	When the moon comes up or at daybreak,
	Ever after we'll live happilee—
	On slices o' cake an' cups o' tea.

A cup o' tea filled to the brim,
Suits Aunt Sally so that suits him.
They don't want a bottle of fancy wine,
Offer them a brewery an' they'll decline.
A slice o' cake, cut it nice an' thick,
Smother it in icing they can lick,
And ever ever after they'll live happilee—

Worzel	On slices o' cake—
All	On slices o' cake—
Aunt Sally	On slices o' cake—
All	On slices o' cake—
Worzel	On slices o' cake—
All	And cups o' tea.

CURTAIN

No. 22. Finale and Walk Down

No. 23. Scarecrow Day (Reprise)

Company

It's a scarecrow day,
Feel the sun and smell the new-mown hay,
It's the sorta day you oughta lie down
And while an hour away.
Scarecrow days,
Days for lazin' sheep, for grazin' days,
It's amazin'
How without even tryin',
You close your eye'n
You're dreamin'
And schemin'
Of a scarecrow day,
Sky of blue has chased the clouds away.

It's the kinda time you find it's sublime
To close your eyes and say
Ho-hey!
Folks call me crazy
But I'll go my way,
'Cos I'm goin' nowhere
On a scarecrow day,
'Cos I'm goin' nowhere
On a scarecrow day.

No. 24. Scarecrow Day (Final Reprise)

CURTAIN

FURNITURE AND PROPERTY LIST

ACT I

SCENE 1

On stage: Scarecrow pole with headless scarecrow

Off stage: Tricycle and basket containing a scarecrow head **(Crowman)**

Personal: **Crowman:** twig in pocket

SCENE 2

On stage: Scarecrow pole and scarecrow with mangel-worzel head and umbrella
Farmhouse cut-out with practical door. *Hanging outside:* washing
Gypsy caravan
Stile

Off stage: 2 full suitcases **(Mr Peters)**
Suitcases etc. **(John and Sue)**
Bowl of pastry mix and spoon **(Mrs Braithwaite)**

Personal: **John:** coin in pocket
Mrs Braithwaite: handkerchief
Mr Peters: wristwatch

SCENE 3

On stage: Scarecrow pole and scarecrow with umbrella
Stile

SCENE 4

On stage: Scarecrow pole
Stile
Bales of hay
Ladder
4 "scarecrow heads" in hayloft
Comics (for **John** and **Sue)**
Tattered umbrella

Off stage: Hot apple pie **(Sue)**

Personal: **Worzel:** robin redbreast (used throughout), new "head"

SCENE 5

On stage: Cottage with balcony, practical doors and windows. *At attic window:* curtains open
Water butt L of cottage
Feather duster (for **Mr Shepherd**)

Off stage: Bicycle. *In basket:* Village Fête posters. *On handlebars:* pot of paste and brush **(PC Parsons)**

SCENE 6

On stage: Colourful banners and streamers
Farmhouse cut-out with practical door
Gypsy caravan
Stile

Off stage: Basket of cakes **(Mrs Braithwaite)**
Mr Peters's old sports jacket **(Sue)**

Personal: **Mrs Bloomsbury-Barton:** large hat

SCENE 7

On stage: Rostrum
Tea-tent exterior with flap entrance
Coconut shy pitch, wooden balls and coconuts
Various side shows

Off stage: Handcart **(Mr Shepherd)**
Bell-rope **(Stage Management)**
Candy-floss **(Aunt Sally)**
Battered telescope **(Crowman)**

Personal: **Mrs Bloomsbury-Barton:** sheaf of notes

SCENE 8

On stage: Scarecrow pole
Farmhouse cut-out with practical door
Stile
Bales of hay
Pile of straw
Skip

Off stage: Apples **(Worzel** and **Aunt Sally)**

Personal: **Worzel:** hedgehog

ACT II

SCENE 1

On stage: **Crowman**'s house cut-out with practical door
Gate to backyard
Antique gas street lamp *In backyard:* various tools including hoe, rake, pitchfork

Off stage: Homing pigeon **(Sergeant Beetroot)**

Personal: **Sergent Beetroot:** alarm clock slung round his waist (used throughout)

SCENE 2

On stage: Bales of hay
Pitchfork

Off stage: Hoe, practical lighted lantern **(Soggy)**
Rake, practical lighted lantern **(Scabby)**
Pitchfork, practical lighted lantern **(Sergeant Beetroot)**

Personal: **Worzel:** bucket over his head

SCENE 3

On stage: Cottage with balcony, practical doors and windows. *At attic window:*
curtains open. *Upstairs:* dummy Aunt Sally
Water butt L of cottage
Pile of potatoes

Off stage: Pitchfork **(Worzel)**
Hoe **(Soggy)**
Rake **(Scabby)**
Pitchfork **(Sergeant Beetroot)**
Ladder with missing rung **(Scabby** and **Soggy)**
Blunderbus **(Mr Shepherd)**
White flag **(Sergeant Beetroot)**
Hat with potatoes embedded in it **(Crowman)**

SCENE 4

On stage: High barn wall. *Against it:* hayfork
Bench

Personal: **PC Parsons:** helmet, notebook and pencil
Mr Shepherd: hat
Mrs Bloomsbury-Barton: handbag, umbrella

SCENE 5

On stage: Door
Loft with ladder
Chairs for jury
Improvised dock
Table. *On it:* gavel, **Crowman**'s hat
Chair
Witness box

Off stage: Large bundle of official papers etc. **(Crowman)**
Potato **(Aunt Sally)**

Personal: **Sergeant Beetroot:** pitchfork
Crowman: box of matches

SCENE 6

On stage: Bales of hay

SCENE 7

On stage: Scarecrow pole

Off stage: Birthday presents **(Scarecrows** and **Sergeant Beetroot)**
Large birthday cake **(Stage Management)**
Enormous birthday cake **(Stage Management)**
Birthday presents **(John** and **Sue)**

Personal: **Crowman:** twig in pocket, flute

LIGHTING PLOT

Practical fittings required: antique gas street lamp for ACT II SCENE 1
Various interior and exterior settings

ACT I, SCENE 1. Just before dawn

To open: Night effect with dawn gradually breaking

| Cue 1 | **Crowman** gesticulates
Lightning | (Page 1) |
| Cue 2 | Scarecrow lurches forward on its post
Lightning, then darkened sky effect | (Page 2) |

ACT I, SCENE 2. Morning

To open: Bright sunshine effect

| Cue 3 | **John** and **Sue** run off
Darken lighting | (Page 6) |

ACT I, SCENE 3. Morning

To open: Darkened effect gradually increasing

| Cue 4 | **John** and **Sue** run off
Lightning | (Page 7) |
| Cue 5 | Farm workers run home
Black-out | (Page 7) |

ACT I, SCENE 4. Morning

To open: Bright sunshine effect

No cues

ACT I, SCENE 5. Morning

To open: Bright sunshine effect

No cues

ACT I, SCENE 6. Afternoon

To open: Bright sunshine effect

No cues

ACT I, SCENE 7. Afternoon

To open: Bright sunshine effect

No cues

ACT I, SCENE 8. Afternoon

To open: Bright sunshine effect

No cues

ACT II, SCENE 1. Afternoon

To open: Bright sunshine effect

Cue 6   **Sue:** "... that Worzel can walk and talk."   (Page 40)
           Evening shadow effect, gradually increasing to dusk

Cue 7   **Crowman** turns up the antique gas street lamp   (Page 44)
           Bring up practical and covering spot

Cue 8   At end of song No. 15   (Page 45)
           Fade to Black-out

ACT II, SCENE 2. Night

To open: Black-out

Cue 9   As **Sergeant Beetroot, Soggy** and **Scabby** enter with lighted
           lanterns   (Page 45)
           Bring up glow effect from lanterns

Cue 10   As **Sergeant Beetroot, Soggy** and **Scabby** move downstage   (Page 46)
           *Bring up bright moonlight effect and snap off lantern effect as
           they extinguish lanterns*

ACT II, SCENE 3. Dawn
To open: Gradually bring up dawn effect

No cues

ACT II SCENE 4. Morning

To open: Bright sunshine effect

No cues

ACT II, SCENE 5. Day

To open: General interior lighting

Cue 11   **Sergeant Beetroot** paces up and down   (Page 57)
           Dim to give eerie shadow effect

ACT II, SCENE 6. Day
To open: Bright sunshine effect
No cues

ACT II, SCENE 7. Day
To open: Bright sunshine effect
No cues

EFFECTS PLOT

ACT I

Cue 1	To open *Mist effect*	(Page 1)
Cue 2	**Crowman** gesticulates *Rumble of thunder*	(Page 1)
Cue 3	**Crowman:** ". . . Worzel Hedgerow Gummidge." *Cawing of rooks*	(Page 2)
Cue 4	**Crowman:** "And I give thee life . . ." *Crack of thunder*	(Page 2)
Cue 5	Scarecrow lurches forward on its post *Thunder*	(Page 2)
Cue 6	**John** and **Sue** run off *Thunder*	(Page 7)
Cue 7	To open SCENE 4 *Rooks cawing, continue to end of scene*	(Page 7)
Cue 8	**Mr Peters** and the children move off *Dog barking*	(Page 19)
Cue 9	**Mrs Bloomsbury-Barton** exits *Dog barking angrily*	(Page 20)
Cue 10	At the end of song No. 6 *Rooks cawing angrily*	(Page 20)
Cue 11	**Worzel** exits *Increase noise of rooks*	(Page 20)
Cue 12	**Worzel:** "Nyah nyah nyah——" *Glass smashing*	(Page 30)

ACT II

Cue 13	**Mr Shepherd** goes into the cottage *Crash of crockery*	(Page 49)
Cue 14	**Soggy** charges through cottage front door and out the back *Crash of buckets*	(Page 49)
Cue 15	**Mr Shepherd** fires the blunderbus *Loud shot*	(Page 49)
Cue 16	**Soggy** and **Worzel** try to get the dummy through the window *Glass smashing*	(Page 49)

Cue 17 **Mr Shepherd** fires the blunderbus   (Page 50)
        Loud shot

Cue 18 **Worzel** throws potatoes   (Page 50)
        Crash of breaking glass

Cue 19 **Mr Shepherd:** "... awful hoot of an owl."   (Page 52)
        Owl hoot

MADE AND PRINTED IN GREAT BRITAIN BY
LATIMER TREND & COMPANY LTD PLYMOUTH
MADE IN ENGLAND